OFFICIAL SQA PAST PAPERS WITH SQA ANSWERS

Standard Grade Foundation and General
ENGLISH

F Reading 1996 to 2001
G Reading 1995 to 1998 and 2000 to 2001
F/G/C Writing 1999 to 2001
with three years' answers or answer tips

© Copyright Scottish Qualifications Authority

Ist Exam paper published in 1995

Published by
Leckie & Leckie Ltd, 8 Whitehill Terrace, St. Andrews, Scotland KY16 8RN
tel: 01334 475656 fax: 01334 477392
hq@leckieandleckie.co.uk www.leckieandleckie.co.uk

Leckie & Leckie Project Management Team: Tom Davie; David Nicoll; Bruce Ryan
Cover Design Assistance: Mike Middleton

ISBN 1-898890-64-1

A CIP Catalogue record for this book is available from the British Library.

Printed in Scotland by Inglis Allen on environmentally friendly paper. The paper is made from a mixture of sawmill waste, forest thinnings and wood from sustainable forests.

® Leckie & Leckie is a registered trademark.

INVESTOR IN PEOPLE Leckie & Leckie Ltd achieved the Investors in People Standard in 1999.

Leckie & Leckie

Introduction

The best way to prepare for exams is to practise, again and again, all that you have learned over the past year. Work through these questions and check your solutions against these *official SQA answers*. But give yourself a real chance and be honest! Make sure you work through each question thoroughly so that you understand how you got the right answer – *you will have to do this in the exam*!

Leckie & Leckie's Standard Grade English Course Notes. Self-expression has many advantages in school, work and our personal lives. These notes help you study and develop reading, writing and talking skills for all occasions.

Contents

Leckie & Leckie has made every effort to trace all copyright holders. If any have been inadvertently overlooked, Leckie & Leckie will be pleased to make the necessary arrangements. Leckie & Leckie would like to thank the following for their permission to reproduce their material:

Ian Burrell for an article from *The Independent* (p 36),
Hodder and Stoughton Publishers for an extract from *Skellig* by David Almond (p 58),
Sally and Richard Greenhill for two photographs (p 130),
Cindy Palmano for a photograph (p 132),
John Tierney for an article from the *New York Times* (p 98),
SMG publishing for an article from *The Herald* and Lesley Donald for the accompanying photograph (p 110),
Catherine Czerkawska for an article from *The Scotsman* and *The Scotsman* for the accompanying photo (p 120),
BMG Music Publishing for a line from *Search for the Hero* by M People (p 152),
"Things can only get better" Words and music by Jamie Petrie and Peter Cunnah © 1992 EMI Music Publishing Ltd, London WC2H 0QY (p 152),
"Let me entertain you" Words and music by Robert Williams and Guy Chambers © 1997 EMI Virgin Music Ltd, London WC2H 0QY (p 152),
Carcanet Press Ltd for two lines from *Miracle on St David's St* from *Selected Poems* by Gillian Clarke (p 152),
JM Dent for two lines from *Poem in October* by Dylan Thomas (p 152),
Polygon Press for 4 lines from *The Storyteller* by Liz Lochead (p 152),
Michael Busselle for a photograph from *Better Picture Guide to Black and White Photography* (p 158),
Magnum for a photograph by Henri Cartier-Bresson (p 160).

0860/101

SCOTTISH CERTIFICATE OF EDUCATION 1996	TUESDAY, 7 MAY 10.50 AM – 11.40 AM	**ENGLISH STANDARD GRADE** Foundation Level Reading Text

Read carefully the passage overleaf. It will help if you read it twice. When you have done so, answer the questions. Use the spaces provided in the Question/Answer booklet.

SCOTTISH EXAMINATION BOARD
©

THE BEAR

1   The bear had been a real danger, though at the time they had all laughed. No, Mama had never laughed, but Lyddie and Charles and the babies had laughed until their bellies ached. Lyddie still thought of them as the babies. She probably always would. Agnes had been four and Rachel six that November of 1843—the year of the bear.

2   It had been Charles's fault, if fault there was. He had fetched in wood from the shed and left the door ajar. But the door had not shut tight for some time, so perhaps he'd shut it as best he could. Who knows?

3   At any rate, Lyddie looked up from the pot of oatmeal she was stirring over the fire, and there in the doorway was a massive black head, the nose up and smelling, the tiny eyes bright with hunger.

4   "Don't nobody yell," she said softly. "Just back up slow and quiet to the ladder and climb up to the loft. Charlie, you get Agnes, and Mama, you take Rachel." She heard her mother whimper. "Shhh," she continued, her voice absolutely even. "It's all right long as nobody gets upset. Just take it nice and gentle, ey? I'm watching him all the way, and I'll yank the ladder up after me."

5   They obeyed her, even Mama, though Lyddie could hear her sucking in her breath. Behind Lyddie's back, the ladder creaked, as two by two, first Charles and Agnes, then Mama and Rachel, climbed up into the loft. Lyddie glared straight into the bear's eyes, daring him to step forward into the cabin. Then when the ladder was silent and she could hear the slight rustling above her as the family settled themselves on the straw mattresses, she backed up to the ladder and, never taking her eyes off the bear, inched her way up to the loft. At the top she almost fell backward onto the platform. Charles dragged her onto the mattress beside her mother.

6   The racket released the bear from the charm Lyddie seemed to have placed on him. He banged the door aside and rushed in toward the ladder, but Charles snatched it. The bottom rungs swung out, hitting the beast in the nose. The blow startled him for a moment, giving Lyddie a chance to help Charles haul the ladder up onto the platform and out of reach. The old bear roared in frustration and waved at the empty air with his huge paws, then reared up on his hind legs. He was so tall that his nose nearly touched the edge of the loft. The little girls cried out. Their mother screamed, "Oh Lord, deliver us!"

7   "Hush," Lyddie commanded. "You'll just make him madder." The cries were swallowed up in anxious gasps of breath. Charles's arms went around the little ones, and Lyddie put a firm grip on her mother's shoulder. It was trembling, so Lyddie relaxed her fingers and began to stroke. "It's all right," she murmured. "He can't reach us." But could he climb the supports? It didn't seem likely. Could he take a mighty leap and . . ? No, she tried to breathe deeply and evenly and keep her eyes fixed on those of the beast. He fell to all fours and, tossing his head, broke off from her gaze as though embarrassed.

8   He began to explore the cabin. He was hungry, obviously, and looking for the source of the smell that had drawn him in. He knocked over the churning jug and licked at it, but Lyddie had cleaned it too well that morning and the bear soon gave up trying. Before he found the great pot of oatmeal hanging over the fire, he had turned over the table and the benches and upended the spinning wheel. Lyddie held her breath, praying that he wouldn't break anything. Charles and she would try to mend things but he was only ten and she thirteen. They hadn't their father's skill or experience and they couldn't afford to replace any of the household goods.

9   Next the beast knocked over a jar of butter. He smacked it across the floor where it hit the overturned bench, but did not shatter.

10   At last he came to the oatmeal, bubbling over the fire. He thrust his head deep into the pot and howled with pain as his nose met the boiling porridge. He threw back his head, but in doing so jerked the pot off the hook, and when he turned, he was wearing it over his head like a black pumpkin. The bear was too stunned, it seemed, simply to lower his neck and let the pot fall off. He danced about the room in pain on four, then two legs, the pot covering his head, the boiling oatmeal raining down his thick neck and coat.

11   He knocked about, searching for the way out, but when he found the open door, managed to push it shut. Battering the door with his pot-covered head, he tore it off its leather hinges and loped out into the dark. For a long time they could hear him crashing through the bush until, at last, the quiet November night gathered about them once more.

12   Then they began to laugh. Rachel first, throwing back her dark curls and showing the spaces where her pretty little teeth had been only last summer. Then Agnes joined in with her shrill four-year-old shout, and next Charles's not yet manly giggle.

13   "Whew," Lyddie said. "Lucky I'm so ugly. A pretty girl couldn't a scared that old rascal!"

14   "You ain't ugly!" Rachel cried. But they laughed louder than ever, Lyddie the loudest of all, until the tears of laughter and relief ran down her thin cheeks, and her belly cramped and doubled over. When had she laughed so much? She could not remember.

Adapted from *Lyddie* by Katherine Paterson

[END OF PASSAGE]

[BLANK PAGE]

F

Total Mark

0860/102

SCOTTISH CERTIFICATE OF EDUCATION 1996

TUESDAY, 7 MAY 10.50 AM – 11.40 AM

ENGLISH
STANDARD GRADE
Foundation Level
Reading
Questions

Fill in these boxes and read what is printed below.

Full name of school or college

Town

First name and initials

Surname

Date of birth
Day   Month   Year

Candidate number

Number of seat

NB Before leaving the examination room you must give this booklet to the invigilator. If you do not, you may lose all the marks for this paper.

SCOTTISH
EXAMINATION
BOARD

Marks

QUESTIONS

Write your answers in the spaces provided.

Look at Paragraphs 1 to 3.

1. **Write down** an expression which shows that the children laughed a lot about the bear.

   _____   2 ■ 0

2. (*a*) Why might it be Charles's fault that the bear gets into the cabin?

   _____   2 ■ 0

   (*b*) Why might it not be Charles's fault?

   _____   2 ■ 0

3. What is Lyddie doing when the bear appears?

   _____   2 ■ 0

4. **Write down three** things about the bear which Lyddie notices.   2 1 0

   (i) _____

   (ii) _____

   (iii) _____

Look at Paragraph 4.

5. Complete the following sentences about Lyddie's instructions to the family.

   (i) Everyone is to be_____ and move _____ .   2 1 0

   (ii) They are to climb the_____ up to the _____ .   2 1 0

   (iii) Mama is to take_____ and Charles is to take_____ .   2 1 0

PAGE TOTAL

6. How can you tell that the mother is afraid?

_____

2 ■ 0

7. Write down an expression which shows that Lyddie gives the instructions **very** calmly.

_____

2 1 0

Look at Paragraphs 5 and 6.

8. How does Lyddie try to keep the bear's attention away from the family?

_____

2 ■ 0

9. Which **two** things tell Lyddie that the family is up in the loft?

2 1 0

(i) _____

(ii) _____

10. Write down one word which shows that Lyddie climbs the ladder slowly.

2 ■ 0

11. Explain fully how Lyddie and Charles get the chance to pull up the ladder.

_____

_____

2 1 0

Look at Paragraph 7.

12. "'It's all right,' she murmured. 'He can't reach us.'"

What **two** thoughts does Lyddie have which show she is not as confident as she sounds?

2 1 0

(i) _____

(ii) _____

PAGE
TOTAL

Marks

Look at Paragraphs 8 and 9.

13. Give **two** reasons why Lyddie prays that the bear won't break anything.

| | 2 | 1 | 0 |

(i) _____

(ii) _____

14. **Write down three** things the bear disturbs as he explores the cabin.

| | 2 | 1 | 0 |

(i) _____

(ii) _____

(iii) _____

Look at Paragraph 10.

15. Why does the bear howl with pain?

_____

| | 2 | ■ | 0 |

16. Why doesn't the bear simply let the pot fall off its head?

_____

| | 2 | ■ | 0 |

Look at Paragraphs 11 to 14.

17. Which **three** words tell us the bear makes a great deal of noise because it cannot see properly?

| | 2 | 1 | 0 |

(i) _____

(ii) _____

(iii) _____

18. Give **two** reasons for the children's laughter.

| | 2 | 1 | 0 |

(i) _____

(ii) _____

PAGE
TOTAL

Marks

Think about the passage as a whole.

19. In Paragraph 1 we are told that the story took place in 1843.

    Write down three other pieces of information which suggest that it happened a long time ago.

    2 | 1 | 0

    (i) _____

    (ii) _____

    (iii) _____

20. Read the following statements and then tick (✓) to show whether each is **TRUE**, **FALSE** or **CANNOT TELL** from the passage.

	TRUE	FALSE	CANNOT TELL			
When he stood up, the bear's nose almost touched the loft.				2	■	0
The father of the family had gone hunting.				2	■	0
Agnes had dark hair with curls.				2	■	0
Afterwards, everyone laughed except the mother.				2	■	0

21. Apart from giving instructions to the family, what else shows that Lyddie is a responsible and capable girl? Give **two** examples.

    2 | 1 | 0

    (i) _____

    (ii) _____

[END OF QUESTION PAPER]

PAGE TOTAL

FOR OFFICIAL USE

p2 ☐

p3 ☐

p4 ☐

p5 ☐

TOTAL MARK ☐

[BLANK PAGE]

F

0860/101

| SCOTTISH
CERTIFICATE OF
EDUCATION
1997 | WEDNESDAY, 7 MAY
10.50 AM – 11.40 AM | ENGLISH
STANDARD GRADE
Foundation Level
Reading
Text |

Read carefully the passage overleaf. It will help if you read it twice. When you have done so, answer the questions. Use the spaces provided in the Question/Answer booklet.

SCOTTISH
QUALIFICATIONS
AUTHORITY

MCB 0860/101 6/35310

The following article has been adapted from "The Scotsman".

Close of the

CHRIS ROGERS of *Newsround*

1   SCHOOLCHILDREN from all over Europe have taken part in an exciting three days of learning all about space travel — and their teachers were real astronauts, speaking to them from space!

2   The children were chosen from the 14 member countries of the European Space Agency, which was set up in 1980 to put European missions into space. Representing Britain were pupils from Blue Coat School, Coventry, and Kemnal Technology College, Kent. A live link-up with Russia's Mir space station was established at Disneyland, Paris. I was there too, to join the 600 children who touched down at Paris for the weekend of space events.

3   One pupil per country was chosen to question the astronauts on the Mir space station, which is orbiting nearly 200 miles above the Earth. The station was launched to enable long-term experiments to be carried out. Two Russian astronauts on board have been joined by a German.

4   Peter Worden from Kemnal College put the question for Britain. He asked about the worst aspects of space travel . . . "because everything everyone says about space seems to be good", he told me later. "There must be bad things and I want to know them."

5   Every pupil from the chosen schools had to choose a question they wanted to ask the astronauts and then submit it to the organisers at Disneyland. Peter's question was picked, so how did he feel? "Nervous, but I'm more nervous about being live on French television and fluffing my question up," he replied.

6   Throughout the morning, children spoke to other astronauts on the ground and took part in various activities which taught them about the space missions so far. But at midday came the moment everyone had been waiting for and the image of the three Mir astronauts appeared on huge screens.

7   There were claps and cheering as it became clear we had connected with the space station, but there was silence from the screens. "Hello, Mir, can you hear us? It's Paris here," the French presenter shouted — still there was silence.

8   Then, a faint voice could be heard from the speakers and there were more cheers. "Yes, hello Paris, we can hear you now." The

The Mir space station, orbiting nearly 200

encounter
Mir kind

joins in a thrilling link-up with a space station.

looks on the children's faces said it all. We had indeed made contact with three brave men, alone in space.

9 The presenter invited the various children to ask their questions. One from Norway asked what they could see in space now. The astronaut replied, "Well, I'll point the camera out of the window so you can see." After a while it became clear that we were looking at

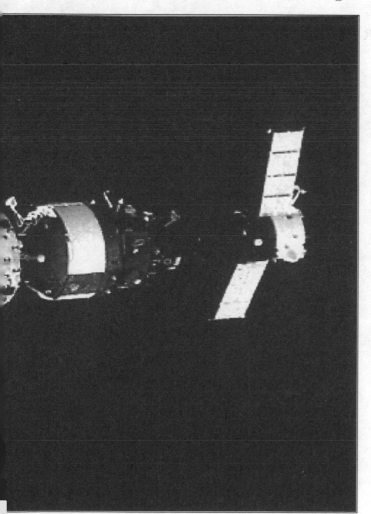

miles above the Earth.

two

planet Earth, with the sun just a momentary glimmer of orange light at the edge of our small planet, followed by total darkness.

10 Then it was Peter's turn. "What's the worst aspect of being in space?"

11 "The feeling of weightlessness is just smashing, fantastic, but it causes many problems," the astronaut replied. "There are some difficulties and life is not easy in space."

12 After the link-up, a spectacular space show rounded off the weekend's activities. Everyone who took part in the weekend seemed to have a special experience to take home with them. One Irish boy told me, "It was great to talk to astronauts in space, something I've always wanted to do."

13 Stephanie from France had a more serious memory of the event. "Being able to talk to people in space is very important for us. We are interested in science and our century is the century of science."

14 As we left the park to go back to the comforts of home we couldn't help but spare a thought for those astronauts. Life in space seemed tough — you even have to go to the toilet upside down!

[END OF PASSAGE]

[BLANK PAGE]

Total Mark

0860/102

SCOTTISH
CERTIFICATE OF
EDUCATION
1997

WEDNESDAY, 7 MAY
10.50 AM – 11.40 AM

ENGLISH
STANDARD GRADE
Foundation Level
Reading
Questions

Fill in these boxes and read what is printed below.

Full name of school or college

Town

First name and initials

Surname

Date of birth
Day Month Year   Candidate number   Number of seat

NB Before leaving the examination room you must give this booklet to the invigilator. If you do not, you may lose all the marks for this paper.

SCOTTISH
QUALIFICATIONS
AUTHORITY

©

MCB 0860/102 6/35310

Marks

QUESTIONS

Write your answers in the spaces provided.

Look at Paragraphs 1 and 2.

1. Where did the children who took part in the weekend of events come from?

    _____   2 ■ 0

2. What did they learn about?

    _____   2 1 0

3. (*a*) What **two** things were unusual about their teachers?   2 1 0

    (i) _____

    (ii) _____

    (*b*) How does the writer's punctuation in Paragraph 1 help to show that the teachers
    were unusual?

    _____   2 ■ 0

4. Complete the following sentences about the events.

    (*a*) The pupils representing Britain came from

    _____

    and _____   2 1 0

    (*b*) The live link-up connected

    _____

    with _____   2 1 0

PAGE
TOTAL

5. (*a*) **Write down** the expression which the writer uses to describe the children's arrival in Paris.

_____

2 ■ 0

(*b*) Why is this a particularly suitable expression to use here?

_____

_____

2 1 0

Look at Paragraphs 3 to 5.

6. What is the purpose of the Mir space station?

_____

_____

2 1 0

7. Why did Peter Worden want to know about the "worst aspects of space travel" (Paragraph 4)?

_____

_____

2 1 0

8. Who chose the final questions?

_____

2 ■ 0

9. Give **two** reasons why Peter was nervous.

2 1 0

(i) _____

(ii) _____

Marks

Look at Paragraphs 6 and 7.

10. What **two** things did the children do in the morning?

   (i) _____   2 1 0

   (ii) _____   2 1 0

11. (*a*) What was the **first** sign that the link-up had been made?

   _____

   _____   2 1 0

   (*b*) How did the crowd react?

   _____   2 1 0

   (*c*) What made the situation more tense?

   _____   2 ■ 0

Look at Paragraphs 8 and 9.

12. "The looks on the children's faces said it all." (Paragraph 8)

   What sort of looks do you think were on their faces?

   _____   2 ■ 0

13. How did the astronaut answer the question from Norway?

   _____

   _____   2 1 0

Look at Paragraphs 12 and 13.

14. **Write down one** word which the writer uses to show that the **final event** of the weekend was impressive.

   [   ]   2 ■ 0

PAGE TOTAL

Marks

15. The weekend was a "special experience" for those who took part. (Paragraph 12)

Why was talking to the astronauts special for:

2 1 0

(i) the Irish boy? _____

_____

(ii) the French girl? _____

_____

Think about the passage as a whole.

16. At times, the writer makes us feel sorry for the astronauts in space.

Write down two examples of this.

2 1 0

(i) _____

(ii) _____

17. Read the following statements and then tick (✓) to show whether each is **TRUE**, **FALSE** or **CANNOT TELL** from the passage.

	TRUE	FALSE	CANNOT TELL
The Mir space station has been in orbit since 1980.			
Two of the astronauts were German and one was Russian.			
Fourteen pupils were chosen to ask the astronauts questions.			
The link-up with the astronauts took place at night.			
The astronauts enjoyed the feeling of weightlessness.			

2 ■ 0

2 ■ 0

2 ■ 0

2 ■ 0

2 ■ 0

[Turn over for Questions 18 and 19 on *Page six*

PAGE TOTAL

Marks

18. This article was taken from a newspaper.

    (*a*)   **Write down three** features of it which are typical of a newspaper article.

        (i) _____

        (ii) _____

        (iii) _____

2   1   0

    (*b*)   Explain how any **one** of these features helped you to enjoy the article.

        _____

        _____

        _____

2   ■   0

19. Imagine you had been at the "weekend of space events". (Paragraph 2)

Which event or activity mentioned in the article do you think you would remember best?

Give a reason for your choice.

    _____

    _____

    _____

    _____

2   1   0

[END OF QUESTION PAPER]

PAGE
TOTAL

FOR OFFICIAL USE

p2   ☐

p3   ☐

p4   ☐

p5   ☐

p6   ☐

F

0860/101

SCOTTISH
CERTIFICATE OF
EDUCATION
1998

WEDNESDAY, 6 MAY
10.50 AM – 11.40 AM

ENGLISH
STANDARD GRADE
Foundation Level
Reading
Text

Read carefully the passage overleaf. It will help if you read it twice. When you have done so, answer the questions. Use the spaces provided in the Question/Answer booklet.

MCB 0860/101 6/30210

First Jump

1   After breakfast on a bright, sunny morning, they paraded on the square, each group under its sergeant. Herded aboard trucks, the whole company was transported to Baldoon Aerodrome, where the men were to do their jumps. No one spoke much as they turned from the road and passed a sentry at the gate. Even the high-spirited Tam Devlin crouched down in a corner, with nothing to say for himself.

2   "We're first to jump," Sergeant Bolton informed his group. "Five men will go up with me in ten minutes' time. Hold yourself in readiness."

3   Alex could not still the tremor in his legs as he sat on the grass, waiting until the sergeant returned. His mouth felt like an oven that had long since overheated. Time and again, he looked up into the sky and asked himself why he had volunteered for the paratroops.

4   "Kennedy, Rae, Devlin, Anderson and Myles, follow me!" Sergeant Bolton beckoned to the men in question.

5   Forcing himself to walk steadily, Alex followed the sergeant's lean form to where an enormous balloon hung anchored to the ground. An officer and a corporal handed out parachutes, then ushered the six men into an open cage which was suspended below the balloon.

6   "Five hundred feet, Sergeant!" The officer slammed an iron gate. "I'll fire a Very light when everything's ready down here."

7   "There's nothing to it, lads." Bolton tried to put them at ease. "Dropping drill first though. You will jump one after the other from fixed lines. Each man will make sure that the man in front of him has fastened his line properly. Normally, a man will make certain himself—when his life depends upon it. But we rigidly adhere to the rule that each man will check the man in front."

8   "What about the last man, Sergeant?" Pate Rae's voice betrayed the tension within him.

9   "I'll be here to see to the last man." Bolton spoke easily. "No matter where, or when, you jump, there will always be a dispatcher, who will see to the last man."

10   "We're going up!" Snack Kennedy shouted in alarm. "The balloon's going up!"

11   Under the control of a winch, the balloon ascended into the heavens, carrying its cargo of nervous men. Alex watched the ground fall away from beneath them. White-faced and with his hands gripped tightly around an iron support, he closed his eyes and prayed for the courage to jump when the time came.

12   "Fasten lines!" Bolton's command seemed to come from a very long distance. "Myles! You will go first."

13   Fumbling and shaking, they fastened the safety-clips to a rail above their heads. Its brightness dimmed by the sun, a Very light sizzled into the sky.

14   "Ready!" Bolton smiled. "Take it easy, Myles. I've seen a thousand drop from this balloon and never an accident yet. When you do jump, don't look down—keep your eyes fixed on the sky: it's better that way. Get set!" The sergeant lifted an iron guard rail. "When I say go—jump!"

15   It took a tremendous effort on Alex's part not to turn his eyes downwards as he stood teetering on the edge of the five-hundred foot drop. Fixing his gaze on a woolly cloud high above him, he waited for the order that would launch him into space.

16   "Go!" The command thundered through his whole being.

17   A violent slap on the back and he was falling downwards at a terrific speed.
Something between a sob and a scream issued from his throat as he caught a fleeting
impression of the earth spinning beneath him. There came a tremendous jerk
around his middle and he was floating gently in mid-air, shroud lines taut over his
head. A sensation of complete satisfaction almost overwhelmed him.

18   "It's easy!" Tears of relief flowed down his cheeks.

19   Alex would have willingly stayed in the pleasant position of floating between
Heaven and Earth, but, all too soon, the green grass rushed up towards him at a
tremendous speed. Remembering all he had been taught about how to fall, he
relaxed every muscle in his body and prepared to make contact with the earth. He
did not make a "banana"—as a bad landing was termed by the older hands who wore
the red beret. Immediately his boots touched the grass, Alex rolled to one side,
allowed the billowing silk canopy to settle down, then hurriedly gathered it in before
a gust of wind could drag him across the aerodrome. He stood for a minute with all
the emotion drained from his body. His first jump was over and it wasn't so bad,
other than that brief second before the parachute opened. Folding the silk as well as
he could, Alex watched his companions make their jumps. Everyone landed easily
and seemed to be quite happy that, at last, they were past the stumbling-block of
their first jump.

Adapted from *Dropping Zone* by P. Baillie

[END OF PASSAGE]

[BLANK PAGE]

Total Mark

0860/102

SCOTTISH
CERTIFICATE OF
EDUCATION
1998

WEDNESDAY, 6 MAY
10.50 AM – 11.40 AM

ENGLISH
STANDARD GRADE
Foundation Level
Reading
Questions

SCOTTISH
QUALIFICATIONS
AUTHORITY

MCB 0860/102 6/30210
©

Marks

QUESTIONS

Write your answers in the spaces provided.

Look at Paragraphs 1 and 2.

1. **Write down two** words from the first paragraph that tell you this passage is about soldiers.

   [   ]   [   ]   2 | 1 | 0

2. Where were the soldiers going and what **exactly** were they going to do there?

   _____

   _____

   _____   2 | 1 | 0

3. The soldiers were "Herded aboard trucks". What **two** things are suggested by the word "Herded"?   2 | 1 | 0

   (i) _____

   _____

   (ii) _____

   _____

4. (a) **Write down** an expression from **Paragraph 1** that tells you the soldiers were worried.

   _____

   _____   2 | ■ | 0

   (b) Explain fully what Tam Devlin was like **normally**.

   _____

   _____   2 | 1 | 0

PAGE
TOTAL

Look at Paragraphs 3 to 6.

5. Explain fully how you can tell that Alex was as nervous as the other men.

_____

_____

2 1 0

6. From the information given in **Paragraphs 4 and 5**, which **one** of these statements is **true**?

    A   Alex was the second in command of the group.

    B   Alex helped to give out the parachutes.

    C   Alex's second name was Kennedy, Rae, Devlin, Anderson or Myles.

    D   Alex was the first man aboard the balloon.

Write down the correct letter in the box below.

☐

2 ■ 0

7. **Write down three** things that Alex noticed about the balloon.

  (i) _____

 (ii) _____

(iii) _____

2 1 0

8. (*a*) In **Paragraph 6**, why has the writer placed an exclamation mark at the end of the officer's statement, "Five hundred feet, Sergeant!"?

_____

_____

2 ■ 0

   (*b*) Why has he put a capital letter at the beginning of the word "Very"?

_____

_____

2 ■ 0

PAGE
TOTAL

Marks

Look at Paragraphs 7 to 10.

9. (*a*) What **two** things tell you that Sergeant Bolton **knew** his men were worried about the jump?

   (i) _____

   _____

   (ii) _____

   _____

   2 | 1 | 0

   (*b*) **Write down** the expression that tells you that Sergeant Bolton's efforts to make the men relax were **not** working with Rae.

   _____

   2 | ■ | 0

10. What **exactly** was the job of "a dispatcher"?

    _____

    _____

    _____

    2 | 1 | 0

Look at Paragraphs 11 to 14.

11. **Write down** an expression from **Paragraph 11** that suggests the balloon went very high into the air.

    _____

    2 | ■ | 0

12. **Write down** any **two** things Alex did which showed that he was afraid **as the balloon went up**.

    2 | 1 | 0

    (i) _____

    (ii) _____

PAGE TOTAL

Marks

13. How did Sergeant Bolton know that the balloon had reached 500 feet?

_____

_____   2 ■ 0

14. Sergeant Bolton tried several ways to put Myles at his ease.
Write down two of them.   2 1 0

(i)   _____

(ii) _____

Look at Paragraphs 15 to 18.

15. (*a*) **Write down** an expression from **Paragraph 15** that emphasises the dangerous
position Alex was in.

_____   2 ■ 0

(*b*) Explain fully how we know that, in spite of the danger, Alex remembered the
Sergeant's advice.

_____

_____   2 1 0

16. Write down an expression that suggests Alex may have needed help to jump.

_____   2 ■ 0

17. What caused the "tremendous jerk"?

_____   2 1 0

[Turn over

PAGE
TOTAL

Marks

18. The following words describe feelings:

terror   relief   fear

Using each word only once, complete the following sentences.

(i)   In **Paragraph 15**, Alex's main feeling was _____ .   2 ■ 0

(ii) At the **beginning of Paragraph 17**, Alex's main feeling was _____ .   2 ■ 0

(iii) At the **end of Paragraph 17**, Alex's main feeling was_____ .   2 ■ 0

Look at Paragraph 19.

19. Write down two expressions which suggest that Alex would have liked the trip to   2 1 0
the ground to last longer.

(i)   _____

_____
(ii)

20. What are the **two** most important things a paratrooper must do in order to fall   2 1 0
properly?

(i)   _____

_____

(ii) _____

21. Why did Alex have to gather in his parachute quickly?

_____

_____

_____   2 1 0

PAGE
TOTAL

Marks

Think about the passage as a whole.

22. Why is the first jump described as a "stumbling-block" (Paragraph 19)?

_____

_____

_____

2 1 0

23. Using evidence from the passage, explain how **you** would have felt in Alex's position.

_____

_____

_____

_____

2 1 0

[END OF QUESTION PAPER]

PAGE
TOTAL

FOR OFFICIAL USE

p2 ☐

p3 ☐

p4 ☐

p5 ☐

p6 ☐

p7 ☐

TOTAL
MARK ☐

[BLANK PAGE]

0860/101

SCOTTISH
CERTIFICATE OF
EDUCATION
1999

FRIDAY, 30 APRIL
10.50 AM – 11.40 AM

ENGLISH
STANDARD GRADE
Foundation Level
Reading
Text

Read carefully the passage overleaf. It will help if you read it twice. When you have done so,
answer the questions. Use the spaces provided in the Question/Answer booklet.

SCOTTISH
QUALIFICATIONS
AUTHORITY

MCB 0860/101 6/31820

The following passage has been adapted from "The Independent".

"Thank God .

Shipwrecked Briton was losing hope of rescue

1   It was the thud of an Australian fist on the carbon hull of Tony Bullimore's overturned yacht that told him he was not going to die.

2   The British yachtsman had spent four days and four nights in an air-pocket inside his capsized yacht, praying that he would be saved. "I started shouting, 'I'm coming, I'm coming,'" he said. "It took a few seconds to get from one end of the boat to the other. Then I took a few deep breaths and I dived out of the boat."

3   It was the climax of one of the most dramatic sea rescues of all time—and a heroic survival in a cabin perched on boxes with "a little chocolate and a little water" and three feet of seawater lapping around him.

4   The Briton had been stranded in one of the most treacherous parts of the world, more than 1,500 miles from the Australian coast and 900 miles from Antarctica.

5   The conditions in which he had existed were the stuff of nightmares—solitude, pitch

"It was heaven . . . I really never thought I would reach that far."

---

darkness, and absolute silence save for the sound of icy waters sloshing round his feet.

6   Tossed around by giant waves, he nibbled pieces of chocolate and took breaths from a diminishing air supply.

7   When Bullimore emerged into daylight early yesterday morning, the moment was almost spiritual. "It was heaven, absolute heaven," he said. "I really never thought I would reach that far. I was starting to look back over my life and was thinking, 'Well, I've had a good life, I've done most of the things I had wanted to.' If I was picking words to describe it, it would be a miracle, an absolute miracle."

8   Bullimore said he felt he had been "born all over again" and as he began his new life yesterday, heading back to land on board the Australian frigate, HMAS *Adelaide*, he had plenty of opportunity to thank those who had saved him. *Adelaide's* skipper, Captain Raydon Gates, said the rescued sailor's first words had been "Thank God" and "It's a miracle."

9   The Australian rescue team was first alerted to the Briton's plight on Sunday, when a satellite distress signal was picked up from his yacht, *Exide Challenger*. Winds of up to 55 knots had snapped the boat's keel and capsized it. To the very last, the rescuers were not sure whether Bullimore was still on board, or floating on a life-raft, or lost for ever.

10   Thierry Dubois, a French yachtsman who like Bullimore was a competitor in the Vendee Globe round-the-world race, had also sent a distress signal from the same area.

. it's a miracle"

11 In extreme weather conditions, an Australian Orion spotter plane scoured the icy expanse of the Southern Ocean for the two men and the HMAS *Adelaide* began its long rescue voyage from Perth, eventually picking up Dubois from a life-raft on Wednesday evening.

12 Inside *Exide Challenger*, Bullimore was doing his best to help the rescue. From his perch in an air-pocket at the top of the boat's upturned hull, he repeatedly dived into the icy waters to harness his life-raft so that it would not drift away and deceive the rescuers.

13 On Tuesday, however, the rescue operation was distracted when one of Bullimore's emergency beacons was detected some distance from the yacht. But the rescuers continued to hope that the yachtsman had remained with his craft.

14 At 1 am GMT yesterday, shortly after daybreak in the Southern Ocean, *Adelaide* reached the stricken yacht which had been sighted on Tuesday by the spotter plane but with no sign of life.

15 Some of the crew were dispatched in a dinghy and Bullimore heard first the knocking on the hull and then the sound of voices. Plunging once again into the freezing waters, he swam for 15 seconds through the darkness before emerging from beneath the yacht. Captain Gates said, "When he bobbed up alongside the yacht, it was a tremendously exciting feeling throughout the ship."

16 At Bullimore's home in Bristol, news of the rescue was greeted with the popping of champagne corks and tears of joy. "The old dog is alive. He's bloomin' alive," said his wife, Lalel. She said that, despite the terrible anxiety of the past few days, she knew she could not stop her "stubborn" husband going to sea again. "He's his own man. He will do what he wants to do. If he thinks he's got to go on, then he goes on," she said.

17 Although rescue co-ordinators in Australia said yesterday that they were not counting the cost of the operation, it is likely to be in the region of £1m. *Exide Challenger*, valued at £500,000, has been abandoned to a watery grave.

Ian Burrell

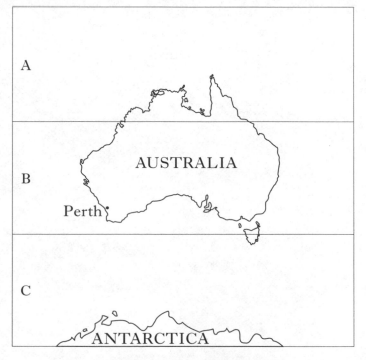

[*END OF PASSAGE*]

[BLANK PAGE]

Presenting Centre No.	Subject No. 0860	Level	Paper No.	Group No.	Marker's No.

F

Total Mark

0860/102

SCOTTISH CERTIFICATE OF EDUCATION 1999

FRIDAY, 30 APRIL
10.50 AM – 11.40 AM

ENGLISH
STANDARD GRADE
Foundation Level
Reading
Questions

Fill in these boxes and read what is printed below.

Full name of school or college

Town

First name and initials

Surname

Date of birth
Day   Month   Year   Candidate number   Number of seat

NB Before leaving the examination room you must give this booklet to the invigilator. If you do not, you may lose all the marks for this paper.

SCOTTISH
QUALIFICATIONS
AUTHORITY

Marks

QUESTIONS

Write your answers in the spaces provided.

Look at the general layout of this passage.

1. What **features of the layout** make it obvious that it comes from a newspaper?

_____

_____   `2 1 0`

2. **Look at the headline**.

    (*a*) In what **two** ways is it typical of newspaper headlines?   `2 1 0`

        (i) _____

        (ii) _____

    (*b*) Why are there inverted commas around the words **"Thank God . . . it's a miracle"**?

    _____   `2 ■ 0`

Look at Paragraphs 1 and 2.

3. Write down **two** separate expressions that suggest Tony Bullimore was in trouble.   `2 1 0`

    (i) _____

    (ii) _____

4. **Explain fully** how Tony Bullimore had been able to breathe even though most of his yacht was under water.

    _____

    _____   `2 1 0`

5. Much of Paragraph 2 is made up of the actual words spoken by Tony Bullimore. How does this improve the report?

    _____

    _____   `2 ■ 0`

PAGE
TOTAL

Marks

Look at Paragraphs 3, 4 and 5.

6. ". . . one of the most dramatic sea rescues of all time . . ." (Paragraph 3)

   (*a*) Reporters often use sensational, exaggerated language like this.
   Write down two other examples from paragraphs 3–5.

   2 1 0

   (i) _____

   (ii) _____

   (*b*) **Write down two facts** given in **Paragraph 4** that suggest this rescue might well have been ". . . one of the most dramatic . . ." ever.

   2 1 0

   (i) _____

   (ii) _____

7. What were the frightening conditions in which Bullimore existed after the yacht overturned?

   _____

   _____

   _____

   2 1 0

Look at Paragraphs 6 and 7.

8. ". . . he nibbled pieces of chocolate . . ."
   Why does the writer use the word "nibbled" here?
   Give **two** reasons.

   2 1 0

   (i) _____

   (ii) _____

[Turn over

PAGE
TOTAL

Marks

9. (*a*) Which **one** of the following words best describes Bullimore's **attitude** when he thought he was **not** going to survive?   Tick (✓) the box.

ACCEPTANCE	
REGRET	
RESENTMENT	
PANIC	

(*b*) Give a reason for your answer.

_____

_____   2 1 0

Look at Paragraphs 8, 9 and 10.

10. ". . . on board the Australian frigate, HMAS *Adelaide* . . ." (Paragraph 8)
Why is the word "*Adelaide*" written in italics?

_____   2 ■ 0

11. (*a*) How did the Australian rescue team first realise Bullimore was in trouble?

_____

_____   2 ■ 0

(*b*) What **three** possibilities did the rescuers then have to consider?   2 1 0

(i) _____

(ii) _____

(iii) _____

PAGE
TOTAL

Marks

12. Why was Bullimore in that area in the first place?

_____

_____   2 ■ 0

Look at Paragraphs 11, 12 and 13.

13. From these paragraphs write down: 2 1 0

    (i)   the **one** word that suggests the thoroughness of the search;

```
┌─────────────────────────────────────┐
│                                      │
│                                      │
│                                      │
└─────────────────────────────────────┘
```

    (ii)   the **one** word that suggests the size of the area to be searched.

```
┌─────────────────────────────────────┐
│                                      │
│                                      │
│                                      │
└─────────────────────────────────────┘
```

14. Why was Bullimore so anxious to keep the life-raft tied to his boat?
Give **two** reasons.   2 1 0

    (i) _____

    (ii) _____

15. Why, despite Bullimore's efforts, was the rescue party almost fooled?
Give **two** reasons.   2 1 0

    (i) _____

    (ii) _____

[Turn over

PAGE
TOTAL

Marks

Look at Paragraphs 14 to 17.

16. How did the rescuers get close to Bullimore's yacht?

_____

_____

2 ■ 0

17. What were the reactions of Bullimore's family to the news of his rescue?

_____

_____

2 1 0

18. Why does Mrs Bullimore describe her husband as "stubborn"?

_____

_____

2 ■ 0

Think about the passage as a whole.

19. Look at the illustration.

Why has a drawing been used rather than a photograph?

_____

_____

2 1 0

20. Look at the map.

It has been divided into three sections: A, B and C.

In the box provided, **indicate the section** in which you think the rescue took place and then, in the space below the box, **explain fully** why you think so.

☐

_____

_____

2 1 0

PAGE
TOTAL

[END OF QUESTION PAPER]

FOR OFFICIAL USE

p2 ☐

p3 ☐

p4 ☐

p5 ☐

p6 ☐

TOTAL
MARK ☐

[BLANK PAGE]

0860/401

NATIONAL
QUALIFICATIONS
2000

TUESDAY, 16 MAY
10.35 AM – 11.25 AM

ENGLISH
STANDARD GRADE
Foundation Level
Reading
Text

Read carefully the passage overleaf. It will help if you read it twice. When you have done so,
answer the questions. Use the spaces provided in the Question/Answer booklet.

SCOTTISH
QUALIFICATIONS
AUTHORITY

©

Adapted from an article by Audrey Ronning Topping.

Charlie, Our M

With a gleam in his eye and mischief in mind, he had us all under his spell.

1   I first met Charlie on Cat Street in Hong Kong. I was browsing for antiques when I heard a terrible screech and turned to see a beggar squatting on the kerb beside a balding, scruffy, white cockatoo.

2   Chained to a wooden perch, the bird was surrounded by children who were teasing him with sticks. The children laughed when the half-crazed creature snapped back at them with his hooked beak, flared his yellow crest and shrieked in Chinese. I was overcome with admiration. This little creature was a fighter.

3   I wanted to rescue him but could not bear the thought of keeping a bird in a cage. As I started to walk away, the cockatoo looked at me imploringly and said, "OK, OK, OK."

4   I was hooked. How did he know I spoke English? After some haggling, I bought him.

5   At home, I removed his shackle. He was grateful and, doglike, began following me round the flat. He couldn't fly because the beggar had cut his flight feathers, so he waddled like a duck and used his beak and claws to hoist himself up our potted trees.

6   In the wild, baby cockatoos learn survival from their parents and other members of the flock. Now, in captivity, Charlie began imitating the only flock he knew, my family.

7   Charlie had a remarkably quick mind and good memory and was soon calling us by name.

8   Every day he picked up new words. His first phrase was "Hello Charlie" and then "Hello" to anyone within range, then "Shut the door!" which soon became "Robin, go back and shut the door."

9   His most frequent word was "Why?" Often when I spoke to the children, Charlie would ask "Why?" just as they did. It drove me crazy. I finally shouted back, "Because I'm your mother!" That became his next phrase.

10   Before long we could see the results of our love and care. Charlie's feathers grew thick and glossy. He developed a confident glint in his eye and established himself as top of the pecking order with our four cats who, to my amazement, restrained their killer instincts even when Charlie stole their food.

11   We were convinced he would never fly again. But one day, after months of watching the children play in the courtyard below the flat, he suddenly dived off the balcony, glided eight storeys down on his crippled wings and made a three-point landing—claws and beak— on the shoulder of Susan.

12   The surprised children shouted, "Super Charlie!" and swung him round in circles on the end of a long stick. He loved it. Soon he called out "Super Charlie" each time he landed in the courtyard.

13   When we moved to Scarsdale, New York State, Charlie became an instant celebrity, greeting everyone with "Hello there! How ya doing?"

14   He slept in the kitchen, where he acted as watchbird, but spent most of his time in an old apple tree in the garden. There he hacked out a large apartment for himself with two entrances and several peepholes. Charlie could not fly up or take off without help, but in the mornings he would hoist himself up with his beak and claws, and glide from tree to tree. In the evening he would call "Audrey!" or "Robin!" until one of us came to bring him inside.

15   Charlie spoke English to us and Spanish to our housekeeper. He meowed to the cats and barked and whistled to our three dogs. They came obediently when he called, and guarded him from stray animals in the garden.

16   Unlike the other members of our family, he was a good listener. We were convinced he could understand everything we said. He could keep a secret, too, so we spilled out all our problems to him. I encouraged this because he was cheaper than a psychiatrist. Eventually we began to think of Charlie as a person of importance.

17   Before I knew it, 25 years had passed.

ad, Bad Cockatoo

18   One clear blue Sunday afternoon we prepared a barbecue in the garden for Joanna's birthday. Charlie was perched on the top branch of a tall tree, with about 20 fat crows he hung out with. They had become friends over the years—Charlie spoke fluent crow and allowed them to share his apples.

19   Surrounded by his crows, Charlie was in his element. Every few minutes he would hang upside down by one leg, flap his wings and shout, "Super Charlie!"

20   Suddenly the calm was shattered by his screams. We looked up to see two large hawks diving out of the sky, straight for Charlie. One hawk grabbed him in its talons and began to fly away.

21   The crows took off after the invading hawks like fighter planes attacking a bomber, cawing to signal other crows to join them. They soon formed a thick black cloud above the hawks and prevented them from gaining height.

22   The evil birdnappers flew out of the garden and headed across a busy street. Joanna and I ran below, shouting and flailing with sticks while the crows flew above, circling and dive-bombing. Motorists screeched to a halt.

23   Finally the crows forced the hawk into a tree. We watched in astonishment as Charlie escaped while his winged allies held the enemy at bay.

24   For one glorious minute, he really was Super Charlie. In his heroic battle, he at last flew high—like the free spirit he was meant to be.

25   Then the second hawk rocketed down, snatching him from above. We heard one last scream. Dear Charlie. He died a champion.

26   That evening, the birthday celebration became a funeral as the whole family gathered to pay respects to one of our own. We saved a few yellow crest feathers and buried him in the garden.

27   Charlie was composed of the stuff that legends are made of, and in our family he has become just that. None of us will ever forget the adventures we shared for 25 years with Charlie Cockatoo.

[END OF PASSAGE]

[BLANK PAGE]

F

Total
Mark

0860/402

NATIONAL
QUALIFICATIONS
2000

TUESDAY, 16 MAY
10.35 AM – 11.25 AM

**ENGLISH
STANDARD GRADE**
Foundation Level
Reading
Questions

Fill in these boxes and read what is printed below.

Full name of centre

Town

Forename(s)

Surname

Date of birth
Day Month Year   Scottish candidate number   Number of seat

SCOTTISH
QUALIFICATIONS
AUTHORITY

©

QUESTIONS

Write your answers in the spaces provided.

Look at Paragraphs 1 and 2.

1. What first drew the writer's attention to Charlie?

    _____

    2 0

2. **Write down two** things which show that Charlie was not well looked after by the beggar.

    (i) _____

    (ii) _____

    2 1 0

3. "This little creature was a fighter." (Paragraph 2)

    (*a*) **Write down three separate words** the writer uses to describe how Charlie reacted when the children teased him.

    2 1 0

    (*b*) How did this behaviour make the writer feel about Charlie?

    _____

    2 1 0

Look at Paragraphs 3 and 4.

4. (*a*) Why did the writer not rescue Charlie immediately?

    _____

    _____

    2 0

    (*b*) What **two** things persuaded her to rescue him?

    (i) _____

    (ii) _____

    2 1 0

5. **Write down** the expression which tells us that the writer did not pay as much as the beggar asked for Charlie.

_____

Look at Paragraph 5.

6. Explain fully why Charlie began following the writer "doglike" round the flat.

_____

_____

7. Explain fully why Charlie had to use his beak and claws to "hoist himself up our potted trees".

_____

_____

Look at Paragraphs 6 to 9.

8. **Write down** the word which the writer uses to compare her family to Charlie's family in the wild.

[   ]

9. What did Charlie do which showed he had "a remarkably quick mind and good memory"? (Paragraph 7)

_____

_____

[Turn over

Look at Paragraphs 10 to 12.

10. How did Charlie's **appearance** and **behaviour** change as a result of the family's love and care?

_____

_____

_____

2
1
0

11. Explain clearly what was amazing about the cats' attitude to Charlie.

_____

_____

2
1
0

12. Explain fully why the children were "surprised". (Paragraph 12)

_____

_____

2
1
0

Look at Paragraphs 13 and 14.

13. Despite becoming an "instant celebrity" (Paragraph 13), what things does Charlie do which remind us he is a bird?

_____

_____

2
1
0

Look at Paragraphs 15 and 16.

14. Explain why the family "began to think of Charlie as a person of importance".

_____

_____

2
1
0

Look at Paragraph 17.

15. Why do you think the writer has made this sentence a short paragraph on its own?

_____

2
0

Look at Paragraphs 18 and 19.

16. Explain fully how Charlie and the crows had become friends.

_____

_____

2
1
0

17. " . . . Charlie was in his element."

Explain how the rest of Paragraph 19 helps you to understand the meaning of this expression.

_____

_____

2
1
0

Look at Paragraphs 20 to 23.

18. (a) **Write down three** expressions the writer uses to make the attack seem warlike.

(i) _____

(ii) _____

2
1
0

(iii) _____

(b) Choose any **one** of these expressions and **explain how well** you think it helps to describe what happened.

_____

_____

2
0

[Turn over

19. "Motorists screeched to a halt." (Paragraph 22)

What **two** things caused this?

(i) _____

(ii) _____

2
1
0

Look at Paragraphs 24 to 27.

20. Write down the word which shows how fast the second hawk moved.

```
┌──────────────────────────────────────────────┐
│                                                │
│                                                │
└──────────────────────────────────────────────┘
```

2
0

21. "For one glorious minute, he really was Super Charlie." (Paragraph 24)

Which expression in this paragraph explains why the writer thought this?

_____

2
0

Think about the passage as a whole.

22. Read the following statements and then tick (✓) to show whether each is TRUE, FALSE or CANNOT TELL from the passage.

	TRUE	FALSE	CANNOT TELL
The Toppings lived in Hong Kong for 25 years.			
The Topping family had three dogs and four cats.			
Charlie died on a Saturday afternoon.			

2
0
2
0
2
0

23. "None of us will ever forget the adventures we shared for 25 years with Charlie Cockatoo." (Paragraph 27)

Which adventure do you think is most memorable and why?

_____

_____

_____

2
1
0

[END OF QUESTION PAPER]

0860/401

NATIONAL
QUALIFICATIONS
2001

MONDAY, 14 MAY
10.35 AM – 11.25 AM

ENGLISH
STANDARD GRADE
Foundation Level
Reading
Text

Read carefully the passage overleaf. It will help if you read it twice. When you have done so, answer the questions. Use the spaces provided in the Question/Answer booklet.

SCOTTISH
QUALIFICATIONS
AUTHORITY

In this extract, Michael and his family have just moved house.

1   I found him in the garage on a Sunday afternoon. It was the day after we moved into Falconer Road. The winter was ending. Mum had said we'd be moving just in time for the spring. Nobody else was there. Just me.

2   He was lying there in the darkness behind the tea chests, in the dust and dirt. It was as if he'd been there forever. He was filthy and pale and dried out and I thought he was dead. I couldn't have been more wrong. I'd soon begin to see the truth about him, that there'd never been another creature like him in the world.

3   I nearly got into the garage that Sunday morning. We called it the garage because that's what the estate agent, Mr Stone, called it. It was more like a demolition site or a rubbish dump. I took my own torch and shone it in. The outside doors to the back lane must have fallen off years ago and there were dozens of massive planks nailed across the entrance. The timbers holding the roof were rotten and the roof was sagging in. The bits of the floor you could see between the rubbish were full of cracks and holes. The people that took the rubbish out of the house were supposed to take it out of the garage as well, but they took one look at the place and said they wouldn't go in it even for danger money.

4   There were old chests of drawers and broken wash-basins and bags of cement, ancient doors leaning against the walls, deck chairs with the cloth seats rotted away. Great rolls of rope and cable hung from nails. Heaps of water pipes and great boxes of rusty nails were scattered on the floor. Everything was covered in dust and spiders' webs. There was mortar that had fallen from the walls. There was a little window in one of the walls but it was filthy and there were rolls of cracked lino standing in front of it. The place stank of rot and dust. Even the bricks were crumbling like they couldn't bear the weight any more. It was like the whole thing was sick of itself and would collapse in a heap and have to get bulldozed away.

5   I heard something scratching in one of the corners, and something scuttling about, then it all stopped and it was just dead quiet in there.

6   I stood daring myself to go in.

7   I was just going to slip inside when I heard Mum calling me.

8   "Michael! What are you doing?"

9   She was at the back door.

10   "Didn't we tell you to wait till we're sure it's safe?"

11   I stepped back and looked at her.

12   "Well, didn't we?" she shouted.

13   "Yes," I said.

14   "So keep out! All right?"

15   I shoved the door and it lurched half-shut on its single hinge.

16   After a while, Mum asked was I coming in for lunch and I said no, I was staying out in the garden. She brought me a sandwich and a can of cola.

17   I finished the drink, waited a minute, then I went down to the garage again. I didn't have time to dare myself or to stand there listening to the scratching. I switched the torch on, took a deep breath, and tiptoed straight inside.

18   Something little and black scuttled across the floor. The door creaked and cracked for a moment before it was still. Dust poured through the torch beam. Something scratched in a corner. I tiptoed further in and felt spider webs breaking on my brow. Everything was packed in tight — ancient furniture, kitchen units, rolled-up carpets, pipes and crates and planks. I kept ducking down under the hose-pipes and ropes and kitbags that hung from the roof. More cobwebs snapped on my clothes and skin. The floor was broken and crumbly. I opened a cupboard an inch, shone the torch in and saw a million woodlice scattering away. I peered down into a great stone jar and saw the bones of some little animal that had died in there. Dead bluebottles were everywhere. There were ancient newspapers and magazines. I shone the torch on to one and saw that it came from nearly fifty years ago. I moved so carefully. I was scared every moment that the whole thing was going to collapse. There was dust clogging my throat and nose. I knew they'd be yelling for me soon so I knew I'd better get out. I leaned across a heap of tea chests and shone the torch into the space behind and that's when I saw him.

19   I thought he was dead. He was sitting with his legs stretched out, and his head tipped back against the wall. He was covered in dust and webs like everything else and his face was thin and pale. Dead bluebottles were scattered on his hair and shoulders. I shone the torch on his white face and his black suit.

20   "What do you want?" he said.

21   He opened his eyes and looked up at me.

22   His voice squeaked like he hadn't used it in years.

23   "What do you want?"

24   My heart thudded and thundered.

25   "I said, what do you want?"

26   Then I heard them yelling for me from the house.

27   "Michael! Michael! Michael!"

28   I shuffled out again. I backed out through the door.

29   It was Dad. He came down the path to me.

30   "Didn't we tell you—" he started.

31   "Yes," I said. "Yes. Yes."

32   I started to brush the dust off myself. A spider dropped away from my chin on a long string.

33   He put his arm around me.

34   "It's for your own good," he said.

35   He picked a dead bluebottle out of my hair.

36   He thumped the side of the garage and the whole thing shuddered.

37   "See?" he said. "Imagine what might happen."

38   I grabbed his arm to stop him thumping it again.

39   "Don't," I said. "It's all right. I understand."

Adapted from *Skellig* by David Almond

[*END OF PASSAGE*]

[BLANK PAGE]

F

Total
Mark

0860/402

NATIONAL
QUALIFICATIONS
2001

MONDAY, 14 MAY
10.35 AM – 11.25 AM

ENGLISH
STANDARD GRADE
Foundation Level
Reading
Questions

SCOTTISH
QUALIFICATIONS
AUTHORITY

QUESTIONS

Write your answers in the spaces provided.

Look at Paragraphs 1 and 2.

1. What time of year was it when the family moved house?

   _____

2. Why do you think the writer finishes the first paragraph with such a short sentence?

   _____

   _____

3. **Write down two things** which made Michael think the man he'd found was dead.

   (i) _____

   (ii) _____

Look at Paragraphs 3 and 4.

4. **Write down three things** from Paragraph 3 which support the idea that the garage looked "more like a demolition site".

   (i) _____

   (ii) _____

   (iii) _____

5. (*a*) Who were supposed to have taken the rubbish out of the garage?

   _____

   _____

   (*b*) Why wouldn't they take it out?

   _____

   _____

6. **Write down three things** from Paragraph 4 which support the idea that the inside of the garage was like "a rubbish dump".

(i) _____

(ii) _____

(iii) _____

2
1
0

7. **Write down** an expression which describes the garage

(i) by smell _____

(ii) as if it had feelings. _____

2
0
2
0

Look at Paragraphs 5 to 15.

8. **Write down two separate words** the writer uses to describe the sounds he hears.

2
1
0

9. (a) Which **one** of the following words **best** describes how Michael felt when his mum called to him?

Tick (✓) the box.

Frightened	
Relieved	
Annoyed	

(b) Give a reason for your answer.

_____

_____

2
1
0

10. Why did Michael's mum want him to keep out of the garage?

_____

2
0

[Turn over

Official SQA Past Papers

11. Why did she **shout** "Well, didn't we?" (Paragraph 12)?

_____

_____

2
1
0

12. In Paragraph 14 why does the writer use an exclamation mark (!) after Michael's mother said "So keep out!"?

_____

_____

2
0

Look at Paragraphs 16 and 17.

13. Michael seemed more determined to enter the garage after lunch.

Why didn't he hesitate this time?

_____

2
0

Look at Paragraph 18.

14. Which word does the writer repeat **in the first four sentences** to add to the mystery and suspense in the story?

```
┌───────────────────────┐
│                       │
│                       │
└───────────────────────┘
```

2
0

15. The writer sometimes exaggerates Michael's description of the inside of the garage.

(_a_) Give **one** example. _____

_____

2
0

(_b_) Explain why you think the writer does this.

_____

_____

2
1
0

16. Complete the following sentences about Michael's feelings.

2
1
0

(i) Michael was _____ in case the garage _____ .

(ii) Michael knew he should _____

2
1
0

because _____ .

Look at Paragraphs 19 to 28.

17. (*a*) Which word **best** describes how Michael would have felt when the man spoke to him?

Tick (✓) the box.

Delighted	
Disappointed	
Surprised	
Shocked	

(*b*) **Write down** the expression the writer uses to show this.

2
1
0

_____

18. What made Michael think that the man hadn't spoken for a long time?

2
0

_____

19. Why do you think Michael "backed out" of the garage?

2
1
0

_____

_____

[Turn over for Questions 20 and 21 on *Page six*

Look at Paragraphs 29 to 39.

20. (*a*) Why did Michael's dad thump the side of the garage?

_____

_____

2
1
0

(*b*) Explain fully why Michael stopped him thumping it again.

_____

_____

2
1
0

Think about the passage as a whole.

21. Give **two** pieces of evidence from the passage which suggest that the man in the garage was **really** unusual.

(i) _____

_____

(ii) _____

_____

2
1
0

[END OF QUESTION PAPER]

0860/34

SCOTTISH CERTIFICATE OF EDUCATION 1995	WEDNESDAY, 3 MAY 1.00 PM – 1.50 PM	ENGLISH STANDARD GRADE General Level Reading Text

Read carefully the passage overleaf. It will help if you read it twice. When you have done so, answer the questions. Use the spaces provided in the Question/Answer booklet.

Timothy, Jane, and their mother, Rose, have found an old cottage with a sign: "FOR RENT OR SALE. APPLY TO BEACH HOUSE, WALLNEY." The children have persuaded Rose—against her better judgement—to enquire about renting it, even though it has stood empty for years.

1   Quarter of a mile up the path, they came to the village of Wallney. Not much of a village: four big farmhouses, a couple of rows of flint-and-brick cottages, pub, sub-post office and an old-fashioned red phone-box. But enough to half-restore Rose's sanity. The owner of the cottage wouldn't want to let it just for a week, or even a fortnight. This was no holiday cottage. The thought brought relief.

2   But there stood Beach House, one of the four farmhouses. Well kept, but not a working farm. Weeds grew in front of the barn doors. Rose walked up the tidy front garden, and knocked on the door of the little glass porch. Too late, she realised the front door was never used. The porch was full of potted plants, several big ones right in front of the door itself.

3   An inner door opened, and a grey-haired woman in spectacles appeared. Respectable-dowdy, with sharp blue eyes and a very stubborn mouth. She gestured angrily, indicating some other entrance that should be used. It put poor Rose one-down from the start. She blundered for a long time round the barns and farmyard, trying to find a way through, until finally the woman opened a door in a six-foot wall, and looked at her as if she was an idiot.

4   "We've come," faltered Rose, "about renting the cottage. Only for a week or a fortnight . . ." She was almost ready to take to her heels and run. Only the small eager figures on each side of her kept her steady.

5   "Oh, come in," said the woman impatiently, and led the way with vigorous but erratic steps, as if she had arthritis but was trying to trample it underfoot by sheer will-power.

6   The kitchen they were led into was uncannily like the one they had just seen in the old cottage, except it was shining and alive. There was a glowing coal fire, which cheered Rose up, even in the middle of July. A grandfather clock ticked soothingly. There was a bundle of knitting in a chair, and a tray laid for tea, with a glass sugar-basin. Various chairs were occupied by various teddy-bears, one wearing full-size spectacles.

7   And straightaway, Rose was under a spell. This indeed was her granny's kitchen come again. She felt very small, but very safe.

8   "Sit down, sit down," said the woman irritably.

9   They sat, careful not to inconvenience the teddy-bears.

10   "We're interested in the cottage, Mrs . . ."

11   "Miss," said the woman decisively, as if that disposed of marriage for good and all. "Miss Yaxley. Were you thinking of renting or buying? Renting is thirty pounds a week; buying is fifteen thousand including the furniture thrown in."

12   Rose gasped at such bluntness.

13   "What's it called?"

14   "Beach Cottage. Belonged to my brother. Just inherited it under his will. *I've* got no use for it. Takes me all my time to keep this place going, at my time of life. Much too much for me. Much too much."

15   "We thought we'd like to try it for a week . . ." said Rose. "To see if the children like it. Then perhaps . . ."

16   She was sure this woman would sweep away her nonsense with a flood of biting common sense. But Miss Yaxley seemed to be very much in two minds. She turned aside, and rubbed at a tiny spot on the chrome teapot, as if it was annoying her intensely.

17   "It's no place for children," she said in a low voice. "My brother was an old man . . ."

18   "I think it's great," said Timothy, turning on his most charming smile like a searchlight. He had a swift eye for adult indecision. But Rose thought for once Timothy had overreached himself. Miss Yaxley gave him a grim look, as if to say children should be seen but not heard. She seemed to come to a decision and Rose was sure the answer would be no.

19   So she was all the more amazed when Miss Yaxley said, "Very well. I don't suppose a week can do any harm." She was still vigorously rubbing away at the spot on the teapot, which showed no sign of moving. Then she said, rather grudgingly but also rather guiltily, "I'll only charge twenty pounds for the first week. You'll have to clean the place up. Men live in *such* a muddle. They're *hopeless*. But I'd like the rent in advance. Weekly in advance."

20   There was more thissing and thatting, but in the end Miss Yaxley drove them back herself in her battered Morris Minor with the dry bird-droppings turning into rust-stains on the bonnet. Rose thought that, having made her mind up, Miss Yaxley was not only keen to get them into the cottage, but also curiously keen to get rid of them.

21   They were done and settled in by nine. The children had truly amazed her. Rose was astonished that children could work so hard. Still, the whole thing *had* been their idea.

22   Timothy, who was practical like his Dad, had discovered a drum of paraffin in a lean-to, filled the oil-lamps and got them going. He used more paraffin, in a careful calculating way that brought her out in a cold sweat, to get the fire in the kitchen range going. He had also got the water-pump over the sink to work. At first it had only made disgusting wheezing sounds, but Tim had poured water down it from a butt in the garden, calling it "priming the pump" very professionally. At first it had pumped evil rusty red stuff, but now it ran clear, though Rose had visions of outbreaks of cholera and typhoid, and hurried dashes to the hospital in Norwich, and how would you ever get an ambulance up that path, but if you boiled all the water . . . Now he was winding up all the clocks and really getting them ticking.

23   And Jane had sweated up the path many times with the luggage and then gone with a huge list of groceries to the sub-post office, and staggered back again, still without complaint, and even thought to buy all available hot-water bottles. And boiled huge black kettles, and shoved all the hotties into the beds, which did seem quite clean, thank God, only awfully dusty and sneeze-making. Now she used the black kettle again to make tea, and settled down to drink hers.

24   "We're a nine-days' wonder in the village," she announced. "Everybody staring at me and yak, yak, yak behind their hands. The woman in the shop asked me how long we were staying, and when I said only a week to start with she said, 'Just as well, my girl, just as well.' What on earth do you think she meant by that?"

Adapted from *Yaxley's Cat* by Robert Westall

[*END OF PASSAGE*]

[BLANK PAGE]

Total Mark

0860/35

SCOTTISH
CERTIFICATE OF
EDUCATION
1995

WEDNESDAY, 3 MAY
1.00 PM – 1.50 PM

ENGLISH
STANDARD GRADE
General Level
Reading
Questions

Fill in these boxes and read what is printed below.

Full name of school or college

Town

First name and initials

Surname

Date of birth
Day Month Year

Candidate number

Number of seat

NB Before leaving the examination room you must give this booklet to the invigilator. If you do not, you may lose all the marks for this paper.

Official SQA Past Papers

Marks

QUESTIONS

Write your answers in the spaces provided.

Look at Paragraph 1.

1. **Write down two** pieces of information which show that Wallney was "not much of a village".

    (i) _____

    (ii) _____

    2 1 0

2. How can you tell from this paragraph that Rose did **not** want to rent the cottage?

    _____

    _____

    2 1 0

Look at Paragraph 2.

3. **Write down two** pieces of information which show that Beach House was "well kept, but not a working farm".

    2 1 0

    (i) Well kept _____

    (ii) Not working _____

4. Explain fully how Rose could tell that "the front door was never used".

    _____

    _____

    2 1 0

Look at Paragraphs 3 to 5.

5. Miss Yaxley seemed unfriendly. **Write down two** expressions which show this.

    2 1 0

    (i) _____

    (ii) _____

6. Describe, **in your own words, two** ways in which Rose was affected by Miss Yaxley's behaviour.

    _____

    _____

    _____

    2 1 0

PAGE
TOTAL

Marks

Look at Paragraphs 6 to 12.

7. The kitchen was "alive". How does the writer develop this idea in the rest of Paragraph 6?

_____

_____

_____   2 | 1 | 0

8. Explain fully why Rose felt "very small, but very safe". (Paragraph 7)

_____

_____   2 | 1 | 0

Look at Paragraph 15.

9. (*a*) From the way Rose spoke, what can you tell about her feelings?

_____

_____   2 | ■ | 0

   (*b*) How does the writer show this?

_____

_____   2 | 1 | 0

Look at Paragraphs 16 to 18.

10. (*a*) Explain, **in your own words,** how Rose expected Miss Yaxley to react to her enquiry.

_____

_____   2 | 1 | 0

   (*b*) How in fact did Miss Yaxley react? Explain as fully as you can.

_____

_____   2 | 1 | 0

PAGE TOTAL

Marks

11. Describe **two** ways in which Timothy tried to persuade Miss Yaxley to let them rent the cottage.

(i) _____

(ii) _____

2 1 0

12. What made Rose think that Timothy had "overreached himself"? Explain **in your own words**.

_____

_____

_____

2 1 0

Look at Paragraph 19.

13. "I'll only charge twenty pounds for the first week." Why did Miss Yaxley say this

(*a*) "rather grudgingly"? _____

_____

2 ■ 0

(*b*) "rather guiltily"? _____

_____

2 ■ 0

Look at Paragraph 22.

14. Give **three** pieces of evidence which show that Timothy was "practical like his Dad".

(i) _____

(ii) _____

(iii) _____

2 1 0

15. **Write down one** expression which shows that Timothy knew what he was doing.

_____

2 ■ 0

PAGE TOTAL

Marks

16. Look at the sentence beginning "At first it had pumped evil rusty red stuff . . .". Show how the writer creates an impression of uneasy thoughts rushing through Rose's mind

(a) by word choice. _____

_____

2 1 0

(b) by sentence structure. _____

_____

2 1 0

Look at Paragraph 23.

17. Write down one word or expression which shows that Jane worked hard.

_____

2 ■ 0

18. Why do you think the writer has used the word "and" so often in the first two sentences of this paragraph?

_____

_____

2 1 0

Think about the whole passage.

19. Think carefully of all you learn about Miss Yaxley.

Tick (√) **one** word from the list below which **you** think describes her best, and give a reason for your choice.

| excitable | | friendly | | unusual | |

| greedy | | patient | |

_____

_____

_____

_____

2 1 0

PAGE
TOTAL

Marks

20. The woman in the shop told Jane it was "just as well" they were staying at the cottage for only a week to start with. (Paragraph 24)

From your reading of the whole passage, explain as fully as you can what **you** think she meant by that.

_____

_____

_____

_____

| 2 | 1 | 0 |

[END OF QUESTION PAPER]

PAGE
TOTAL

FOR OFFICIAL USE

p2 ☐

p3 ☐

p4 ☐

p5 ☐

p6 ☐

TOTAL
MARK ☐

G

0860/103

SCOTTISH
CERTIFICATE OF
EDUCATION
1996

TUESDAY, 7 MAY
1.00 PM – 1.50 PM

ENGLISH
STANDARD GRADE
General Level
Reading
Text

Read carefully the passage overleaf. It will help if you read it twice. When you have done so, answer the questions. Use the spaces provided in the Question/Answer booklet.

SCOTTISH
EXAMINATION
BOARD

MCB 0860/103 6/69210

©

The following article has been adapted from "The Scotsman" newspaper, June 1994.

Washed

1 TWO seagulls hang in the blue sky overhead. For a moment or two they are motionless beneath the white wisps of cloud. One turns its head and screams something to its mate, some seagull joke about the sanity of those humans in the water perhaps.

2 It is 3pm on Saturday and at this precise moment there are three people in the open-air swimming pool at North Berwick, tiny figures bobbing about in the vast blue expanse of water. There are many more shivering beneath towels around the perimeter. The pool was one of the town's most important tourist attractions. They had galas here, swimming and diving displays that pulled in big crowds.

3 It still has its regulars. Two old women turn up with raincoats over their swimming costumes, so they can get into the pool as quickly as possible. Two old men do synchronised swimming. Others bring the staff sweets or baking. But numbers have been falling for years. Costs are high and the season is short. East Lothian District Council is subsidising the swimmers to the tune of almost £10 a time.

4 Now the council has decided to build a modern indoor pool and close one of Scotland's last remaining open-air pools. It has been there since 1900, an essential part of the North Berwick landscape for generations of holiday-makers.

There was a time when almost every swimming-pool, but now long-term future is threatened.

5 There was a time when almost every seaside resort had an outdoor pool, overflowing with noisy, splashing bodies in the summer months. They were part of Scotland. They are part of our social history. But the bodies have disappeared into leisure pools and onto charter flights to Majorca, and the open-air pools have disappeared in their wake.

6 Anstruther, Arbroath, Buckhaven, Macduff, Prestwick, Saltcoats; they all had their own pools. There must have been dozens of them once. There were separate men's and women's pools at St Andrews, but mixed bathing was widely accepted by the time most pools were built in the Thirties when interest in healthy outdoor activities took off.

Cool customers: there is a breeze sweeping across the pool and the teenagers are shivering violently. But then that is because they are speaking to a journalist and not in the warmed water.

away

Scottish seaside resort had an outdoor there are only a few and their BRIAN PENDREIGH reports

7   Portobello Pool opened in 1936 and was considered one of the wonders of the age. It had a diving platform 33 ft above the water, four chutes, four springboards and band music was relayed from Princes Street Gardens. The wave machine was so powerful it soaked the poolside dignitaries on the opening day.

8   The pool became a national attraction and there were 18,000 admissions on a single day, just 4,000 fewer than the number of admissions for the whole of the pool's final summer in 1978. Particularly in the early days, many went merely to spectate or sunbathe, though, unlike some pools, Portobello was heated from the outset, using steam from the adjoining power station. Sean Connery worked as a lifeguard for a while. Now both pool and power station have gone.

9   North Berwick pool will probably open in 1995 for the last time. Other outdoor pools survive at Stonehaven and Gourock, but neither's long-term future is secure.

10   Stonehaven had 86,000 admissions in 1934, its first year, though three-quarters were spectators. Initially the water was unheated, untreated seawater, changed every few days "as it became dirty". The following year it was filtered, disinfected and heated, and the number of people actually going into the pool almost doubled.

11   In 1990, there were 25,000 admissions. In 1993 there were 14,000. The decline would be worse if it were not for the successful reintroduction of special midnight swimming sessions, which had been abandoned in the Seventies because of drunkenness.

12   At North Berwick attendances have fallen steadily over the past five summers, from 21,177 swimmers in 1989 to 8,154 in 1993. "It will be a great sin if this pool Pat Macaulay, who has swum regularly in the pool since childhood and is here with her new season-ticket and her children Richard and Joanna. Pat Macaulay spent the summers of her youth in and by the pool. It was *the* meeting place, *the* social centre for the young people of the town.

13   There is a drop or two of rain in the air and a breeze sweeping across the exposed location beside the harbour. Is it not rather cold? "The water is fine," says Macaulay. "A lot of it is mind over matter . . . I think the kids are getting a bit soft these days."

14   But there are few adults in evidence at this session. The vast majority are children and teenagers, who form lines by the chute and springboard at the deep end.

15   They complain that the new leisure pools do not have these features, the new pools are smaller and the Royal Commonwealth Pool too far away. They are shivering violently. "That's because we're out here speaking to you," says one. "When you're in it's brilliant." Journalistic integrity demands his claim be put to the test.

16   It is not the cold that hits you, but the mouthful of salt water, as you disappear beneath the surface for the first time. The pool is heated, though not as warm as some indoor pools. But some indoor pools are too warm for strenuous swimming. North Berwick is fine as long as you keep moving. There is something quite pleasant in swimming along on your back listening to the chat of the gulls. It is cold when you get out. The knack is to get dried immediately afterwards and not hang around talking to journalists.

17   Shona MacDonald, the pondmaster, and her assistant Michelle Smith have an enormous affection for North Berwick. "The people love it here," Smith says. "We would buy it ourselves if we had the money."

18   However, East Lothian's director of leisure and tourism, says: "Outdoor pools are very expensive to run and declining in terms of attractiveness."

19   The council is building an indoor pool at Musselburgh and is not reopening the outdoor pool at nearby Port Seton. Work has begun on a £2 million pool beside North Berwick's sports centre with opening scheduled for 1996. It will be open all the year round and is expected to have at least 75,000 admissions annually.

20   The director accepts there is some regret in the town at the decision to close the open-air pool, but adds that there have been no formal protests. "People are just being rather nostalgic. The pool has had its day. It's part of a former era."

21   Within the next few years the area occupied by the open-air pool may be returned to its natural state of rocks and sea. The gulls will have a different landscape to discuss. Only rocks and sea remain forever, but the old landscape will undoubtedly linger in the memory of all those whose guts filled with seawater on a chilly Scottish summer's day.

[END OF PASSAGE]

[BLANK PAGE]

FOR OFFICIAL USE

Presenting Centre No.	Subject No. 0860	Level	Paper No.	Group No.	Marker's No.

G

Total Mark

0860/104

SCOTTISH
CERTIFICATE OF
EDUCATION
1996

TUESDAY, 7 MAY
1.00 PM – 1.50 PM

ENGLISH
STANDARD GRADE
General Level
Reading
Questions

Fill in these boxes and read what is printed below.

Full name of school or college

Town

First name and initials

Surname

Date of birth
Day Month Year

Candidate number

Number of seat

**NB Before leaving the examination room you must give this booklet to the invigilator.
If you do not, you may lose all the marks for this paper.**

SCOTTISH
EXAMINATION
BOARD

©

Marks

QUESTIONS

Write your answers in the spaces provided.

Look at Paragraphs 1 to 4.

1. According to the writer, what might the seagulls think of the people in the water?

_____

2   ■   0

2. In Paragraph 2, the writer tells us that there are only three people in the water. Why do you think he also mentions the exact time, and the day?

_____

2   ■   0

3. **Write down** an expression which emphasises the size of the open-air pool at North Berwick.

_____

2   ■   0

4. How can you tell that there are no longer galas at the pool?

_____

2   ■   0

5. Give **two** reasons why East Lothian District Council decided to close the open-air pool.

2   1   0

   (i) _____

   (ii) _____

6. The open-air pool has been "an essential part of the North Berwick landscape for generations of holiday-makers".

   Write down an expression from earlier in this section which conveys the same idea.

_____

_____

2   ■   0

Look at Paragraphs 5 and 6.

7. "There was a time when almost every seaside resort had an outdoor pool . . ."

   Explain how the writer continues this idea in paragraph 6.

_____

2   1   0

PAGE
TOTAL

Marks

8. **In your own words**, explain the reasons given for the disappearance of open-air pools.

_____

_____

_____

2 1 0

Look at Paragraphs 7 and 8.

9. **Write down three** pieces of information which show why Portobello Pool was considered "one of the wonders of the age".

2 1 0

(i) _____

(ii) _____

(iii) _____

10. **Write down** an expression which shows that Portobello Pool was popular with people from all over the country.

_____

2 ■ 0

Look at Paragraphs 10 and 11.

11. **In your own words**, give **two** reasons why the number of swimmers at Stonehaven Pool increased in 1935.

2 1 0

(i) _____

(ii) _____

12. What was the effect of the "reintroduction of special midnight swimming sessions"?

_____

_____

2 1 0

Look at Paragraphs 12 and 13.

13. How do the attendance **figures** given in paragraph 12 show that the writer is closely interested in North Berwick Pool?

_____

2 ■ 0

PAGE TOTAL

Marks

14. Pat Macaulay says, "This is character-building stuff in here".
Write down something else she says which continues this idea.

_____   2 ■ 0

15. "It was *the* meeting place, *the* social centre . . ." (Paragraph 12)
The writer uses italics to show that the word "*the*" has a particular meaning here.
What do you think that meaning is?

_____   2 ■ 0

Look at Paragraphs 14 to 16.

16. What things do young people dislike about the new leisure pools?

_____

_____   2 1 0

17. "When you're in it's brilliant." (Paragraph 15)
(*a*) How does the writer test this claim?

_____   2 ■ 0

(*b*) Explain why he feels the need to test it.

_____

_____   2 1 0

18. (*a*) **Write down two** things the writer seems to like about North Berwick Pool.   2 1 0

(i) _____

(ii) _____

(*b*) **Write down two** things he seems to dislike about it.   2 1 0

(i) _____

(ii) _____

PAGE
TOTAL

Marks

Look at Paragraph 20.

19. ". . . there is some regret . . . at the decision to close the open-air pool"

    (a) **Write down** another expression from this paragraph which indicates people's feelings about the closure.

    _____

    2 ■ 0

    (b) Explain **in your own words** what this expression tells you about people's feelings.

    _____

    _____

    2 1 0

Think about the passage as a whole.

20. This article was taken from a newspaper.

    Write down any **three** features of it which are typical of a newspaper article.

    (i) _____

    (ii) _____

    (iii) _____

    2 1 0

21. Explain how the title relates to the content of the passage.

    _____

    _____

    _____

    2 1 0

22. (a) What unusual idea does the writer use at the beginning and ending of the passage?

    _____

    _____

    2 1 0

    (b) What effect does this have?

    _____

    _____

    2 ■ 0

[END OF QUESTION PAPER]

PAGE
TOTAL

FOR OFFICIAL USE

p2 ☐

p3 ☐

p4 ☐

p5 ☐

TOTAL
MARK ☐

0860/103

SCOTTISH CERTIFICATE OF EDUCATION 1997	WEDNESDAY, 7 MAY 1.00 PM – 1.50 PM	ENGLISH STANDARD GRADE General Level Reading Text

Read carefully the passage overleaf. It will help if you read it twice. When you have done so, answer the questions. Use the spaces provided in the Question/Answer booklet.

SCOTTISH
QUALIFICATIONS
AUTHORITY

Tunes For Bears To Dance To

1   Henry had been impatient for the cast to be removed so that he could return to his job as the bender for Mr Hairston at the Corner Market. Mr Hairston had a back problem and found it hard to bend over. Henry did the bending for him. Picked up whatever fell on the floor. Reached for merchandise on the lower shelves to fill the customers' orders. He also had other duties. Helped unload the boxes and crates that arrived from the wholesalers. Stocked the shelves. Bagged the potatoes in the cellar, then carried them upstairs to the produce section. Mr Hairston was proud of his produce. Fresh lettuce and carrots and spinach and such extras as parsnips and mushrooms, all of them in neat display at the rear of the store.

2   Henry worked at the store every day after school and on Saturday mornings. Until, that is, he had broken his kneecap, tripping, then falling down the bottom steps of the house just as school ended in June. A hair-line fracture, the doctor had said, nothing serious, but serious enough for a cast that enclosed his calf and knee. Mr Hairston said he would keep his job open until his knee was healed.

3   "How will you bend over?" Henry had asked.

4   "I won't stock the lower shelves until you come back."

5   "Who'll sweep the floors and put up the potatoes?"

6   Mr Hairston had scowled without answering. He scowled most of the time, his expression as sour as the pickles in the wooden barrel near the cash register.

7   Five weeks later when Henry reported to the store without his crutches, ready for work, Mr Hairston merely grunted.

8   "Potatoes to bag up," he called over the shoulder of a customer, and Henry made his way down to the cellar, where a bin of potatoes awaited him. He always tried to hurry the job because the cellar was dark and damp and he often heard rats scurrying across the floor. One day, a grey rat squirted out of a bag of potatoes and Henry had leapt with fright, his heart exploding in his chest. He was afraid of a lot of things — the closet door that never stayed closed in his bedroom, spooky movies about vampires — but most of all, the rats.

9   When he came back upstairs, Mr Hairston was saying goodbye to a customer Henry recognized as Mrs Pierce, who lived on the first floor of his tenement. Smiling and nodding, Mr Hairston led her to the door and closed it softly after her.

10   "Disgusting, the wart on her chin, hairs growing out of it," he said, returning to the register, a sneer replacing the smile. Actually, his smile was merely a rearrangement of his lips, his usual sneer turned inside out. Henry was amazed at how Mr Hairston treated his customers.

11   "The customer's always right," he proclaimed one day, as if he could read Henry's mind. "But only in the store. When buying. Otherwise, they're only people. Stupid, most of them. Don't even know a bargain when they see one. So, why give them a bargain?"

12   He handed Henry a candy bar, which astounded the boy because Mr Hairston had never before given him a treat. "Eat," he said. Then, "It was nice with the customers during the war, though. Rationing. People came running if they heard I had got butter in. Or cigarettes."

13   Henry listened, his cheeks bulging with the candy while Mr Hairston looked off, as if he were talking to himself, his voice almost dreamy. "I'd make them line up. Make them wait, acting like the stuff hadn't arrived yet but was expected any minute. All the time the order was here and they waited in line. I was like a dictator, the way they treated me. I *was* a dictator. Because I had control over them." Then looking down as if discovering Henry's presence after having forgotten him there, he said, "Go to work. I don't pay you to hang around doing nothing."

14   Just before closing time, while Henry was sweeping the floor, Mr Hairston's daughter came into the store. She appeared at the back door, having descended from the tenement above, where Mr Hairston lived with his wife, whom Henry had never seen, and the girl, whose name was Doris. Doris was a whisper of a girl, slender, with long black curls that reached her shoulders, a bow in her hair. It always looked like the same bow but the colours were different, red and yellow and blue, bright and vivid colours in contrast with her pale, white face, the dark eyes deep in their sockets, like the windows of a haunted house.

15   She usually came and went like a ghost, appearing suddenly and then fading away, a door closing softly behind her or the rustle of her clothing faint in the air. Sometimes he didn't see her at all but sensed her presence somewhere in the store. She was a year ahead of him in school and when they met in the corridor she lowered her eyes and looked away. She always carried library books in her arms. In the store he sometimes felt those haunted eyes upon him, turned and almost saw her, then heard the back door closing softly. They had never spoken a word to each other.

16   Whenever Mr Hairston saw her in the store, he would order her to leave. "Upstairs," he'd command, his hand pointing to the ceiling.

17   That afternoon the girl spoke to Henry for the first time, a brief word, "Hello." So brief and whispered that at first he doubted his ears. She didn't smile at him but her expression changed, or rather an expression of some kind filled the usual blankness of her face. He could not read that expression. As she turned away before he could return her greeting — if it *had* been a greeting — he noticed a bruise on her cheek, purple and ugly.

18   "What happened to your cheek?" he asked, whispering for some reason.

19   "Upstairs!"

20   Mr Hairston's voice was like thunder in the quiet store and Henry leapt with surprise as he turned to confront the store owner, whose face was dark with anger.

21   Henry began to sweep furiously and heard the girl's footsteps fading, the door opening and closing.

22   "She fell down," Mr Hairston said while Henry swept the same spot over and over. "Clumsy girl, always hurting herself."

23   A late customer entered the store and Mr Hairston turned away, cursing beneath his breath. He hated last-minute customers.

24   That night Henry thought of Doris, who was clumsy and fell down a lot and hurt herself. He prayed to keep her safe from harm.

Adapted from *Tunes For Bears To Dance To* by Robert Cormier

[END OF PASSAGE]

[BLANK PAGE]

Total Mark

0860/104

SCOTTISH
CERTIFICATE OF
EDUCATION
1997

WEDNESDAY, 7 MAY
1.00 PM – 1.50 PM

**ENGLISH
STANDARD GRADE**
General Level
Reading
Questions

Fill in these boxes and read what is printed below.

Full name of school or college

Town

First name and initials

Surname

Date of birth
Day Month Year

Candidate number

Number of seat

**NB Before leaving the examination room you must give this booklet to the invigilator.
If you do not, you may lose all the marks for this paper.**

Marks

QUESTIONS

Write your answers in the spaces provided.

Look at Paragraphs 1 and 2.

1. Why had Henry been "impatient"?

    _____

    _____   2 1 0

2. Why did Mr Hairston need a "bender"?

    _____

    _____   2 1 0

3. (a) **Write down three** things Henry did as part of his "other duties".   2 1 0

        (i) _____

        (ii) _____

        (iii) _____

    (b) How does the writer's sentence construction in Paragraph 1 draw attention to
         the variety of actions Henry has to carry out?

         _____

         _____   2 1 0

Look at Paragraphs 7 and 8.

4. **In your own words** describe how Mr Hairston first greeted Henry on his return to
    work.

    _____

    _____   2 1 0

5. What **three** things did Henry dislike about the cellar?   2 1 0

        (i) _____

        (ii) _____

        (iii) _____

PAGE
TOTAL

Marks

6. ". . . a grey rat squirted out of a bag of potatoes . . ." (Paragraph 8)

    (*a*) What is unusual about the writer's use of the word "squirted" in this sentence?

    _____   2 ■ 0

    (*b*) Why is it a particularly suitable word to use here?

    _____   2 ■ 0

Look at Paragraphs 9 to 11.

7. (*a*) Describe Mr Hairston's **behaviour** and **attitude** towards Mrs Pierce while she
    was in his shop.   2 1 0

    (i) Behaviour _____

    _____

    (ii) Attitude _____

    _____

    (*b*) Explain fully how these changed once she had left.   2 1 0

    (i) Behaviour _____

    _____

    (ii) Attitude _____

    _____

8. **Write down** the **one** word the writer uses which most clearly shows that
    Mr Hairston's smile was not genuine.

    ┌─────────────────────────────────┐
    │   │
    └─────────────────────────────────┘   2 ■ 0

9. (*a*) What is unusual about the writer's sentence construction in Paragraph 11?

    _____   2 ■ 0

    (*b*) What does the writer's use of this construction suggest about Mr Hairston's
    character?

    _____   2 ■ 0

PAGE
TOTAL

Marks

Look at Paragraphs 12 and 13.

10. (*a*) What was Mr Hairston's **real** reason for thinking "it was nice with the customers during the war"?

_____

2   1   0

(*b*) Give an example of his behaviour which supports your answer to (*a*).

_____

2   ■   0

11. While talking about wartime, Mr Hairston "looked off . . . his voice almost dreamy".
    What else did he do which suggests he had been day-dreaming?

_____

2   ■   0

Look at Paragraphs 14 and 15.

12. (*a*) Doris is described as a "whisper" of a girl.
    What do you think the writer means by this?

_____

2   ■   0

(*b*) In Paragraph 14, what comparison does the writer use to describe her eyes?

_____

2   ■   0

(*c*) **Write down three** other words or expressions from Paragraph 15 which the writer uses to convey a similar idea about Doris.

2   1   0

(i) _____

(ii) _____

(iii) _____

13. **Write down** the **two separate words** which best convey the contrast between Doris's face and her bows.

[   ]   and   [   ]

2   ■   0

14. Give **two** pieces of evidence which suggest that Doris was shy.

2   1   0

(i) _____

(ii) _____

PAGE
TOTAL

Marks

Look at Paragraphs 17 and 18.

15. (*a*) What unusual thing happened that afternoon?

_____   2 1 0

(*b*) Explain **in your own words** why Henry "doubted his ears".

_____

_____   2 1 0

(*c*) **Write down** an expression from later in Paragraph 17 which repeats this idea of doubt.

_____   2 ■ 0

16. When Henry asked Doris about her cheek, he whispered "for some reason". What reason do you think he had for whispering?

_____   2 ■ 0

Look at Paragraphs 20 to 24.

17. Mr Hairston's face was "dark with anger". What other expression is used in this paragraph to show his anger?

_____   2 ■ 0

18. "Henry began to sweep furiously" (Paragraph 21)
"... Henry swept the same spot over and over" (Paragraph 22)
What do Henry's actions tell you about how he felt?

_____

_____   2 1 0

19. "'She fell down,' Mr Hairston said ..." (Paragraph 22)
From your reading of the whole passage, do you believe Mr Hairston? Give a reason for your answer.

_____

_____

_____

_____   2 1 0

[END OF QUESTION PAPER]

PAGE
TOTAL

FOR OFFICIAL USE

p2 ☐

p3 ☐

p4 ☐

p5 ☐

TOTAL
MARK ☐

G

0860/103

SCOTTISH
CERTIFICATE OF
EDUCATION
1998

WEDNESDAY, 6 MAY
1.00 PM – 1.50 PM

ENGLISH
STANDARD GRADE
General Level
Reading
Text

Read carefully the passage overleaf. It will help if you read it twice. When you have done so, answer the questions. Use the spaces provided in the Question/Answer booklet.

Why You Don't See Baby Pigeons

1   When I moved to a flat in New York and discovered that my new neighbours included a colony of pigeons, my first reaction was: exterminate the brutes! I cringed at their morning mating calls, and agreed with my wife, Dana, when she cursed them as winged rodents that soil the city. I attacked them with broom and water-pistol. It was hard for me to believe that the traditional symbol of peace, a dove with an olive branch, is actually a white pigeon.

2   Then last December, after scaring away a grey pigeon roosting on the sill of our bathroom window, I found a nest there with an egg in it. "Revenge is ours!" I shouted to Dana, triumphantly holding the egg aloft. "Should I smash it right away or save it for an omelette?"

3   But Dana was looking in horror at the window-sill behind me. The pigeon had swooped back to the empty nest and was beating its wings against the window frame.

4   "You put that back this second!" Dana said, with the same look on her face that I swear the parent pigeon had.

5   "How can a rational human want to save a baby pigeon?" I asked as I returned the egg.

6   And then it came to me. Here was a chance to answer the perennial mystery that puzzled generations of city dwellers: why doesn't anyone ever see a baby pigeon? Let others plumb Loch Ness for its monster or climb the Himalayas in search of the Yeti. I would be the first human to see a baby pigeon in the wild.

7   The bird roosted outside the bathroom for a week, and then one morning the nest was empty—no mother, no baby, no egg. Soon another nest appeared with two eggs, but they, too, vanished.

8   I began keeping a field journal, and named the grey pigeon Medea and her black-and-white speckled partner Don Guano. On March 12 Don Guano strutted about, following Medea in circles around the living-room ledge. Finally he mounted her for a second or two, flapping his wings—for balance, I suppose, unless he was just happy.

9   Two days later an egg appeared, followed shortly by a second. Don Guano and Medea settled into a domestic routine. From late morning until late afternoon he sat on the eggs while she went off. The rest of the time, she roosted while he brought twigs for home-improvement projects.

10   Then, after ten days of roosting, Don Guano and Medea abruptly abandoned the nest. The next day the eggs were gone without a trace.

11   I reported the parenting troubles to Margaret Barker of the Cornell Laboratory of Ornithology. "Eggs normally hatch after 18 days," she said, "but sometimes pigeons are frightened off the nest, and sometimes eggs never hatch because the parents aren't getting the proper diet to make sturdy eggshells."

12   "And why," I asked, "do we never see a baby pigeon?" "They stay in the nest for the first month," Margaret told me, "and grow so rapidly they're nearly full size when they emerge."

13   When Medea returned, I fed her a bowl of cereal mixed with a powdered calcium supplement. I worried about what this was doing to me. Was I becoming one of those people on park benches who feed pigeons?

14   Soon the calcium-enriched Medea laid two more eggs, and this time the roosting proceeded smoothly for the full 18 days. We were ready to make history on Friday, April 21. I armed myself with a new pair of binoculars and a copy of *The Pigeon* by Wendell Mitchell Levi, which I studied with all the care other parents devote to Dr Spock's books.

15   "Wherever civilisation has flourished, there the pigeon has thrived," wrote Levi. Pigeons are found on every continent except Antarctica, inhabiting environments from Alaska to the equatorial islands. They were worshipped in Mesopotamia and sculpted on Egyptian tombs. They carried messages for King Solomon, helped Julius Caesar conquer Gaul and won dozens of medals for combat service during the Second World War.

16   Pigeons, or "rock doves", can fly up to 75 miles per hour and find their way home from more than 1000 miles away. Their primary reference seems to be the position of the sun, which correlates with a pigeon's biological clock. But they can navigate even under overcast skies by sensing the earth's magnetic field. There are "reverse commuter" pigeons, urban pigeons that fly 30 miles a day to fields and grain silos outside the city, then return to roost in town.

17   They are social animals, living in colonies because they gain protection from predators. Poets have praised pigeons' lifelong devotion to their mates. Tennyson linked their iridescent feathers with romance and rebirth in his famous couplet:

> *In the spring a livelier iris changes on the burnish'd dove;*
> *In the spring a young man's fancy lightly turns to thoughts of love.*

18   I quoted those lines to Don Guano and Medea as we waited on that crucial Friday in April. But by evening, neither egg had hatched. I feared the worst. Next day at noon, however, as I watched Don Guano settle in for his shift on the nest, I spotted a bit of golden fuzz moving underneath him.

19   It was a shaggy little creature, lying in a heap along with the eggshell it had just escaped. "Miracle of miracles!" I wrote in my journal. "Yes, New York, there is a baby pigeon." I had never been an animal lover and was not particularly fond of naturalists or the endangered species they were trying to save. So why pigeons?

20   The answer did not occur to me until I visited New York's most glamorous bird, the peregrine falcon, 57 floors above the streets. There was no doubting this bird's power, particularly after seeing the ***pigeon*** feathers in the nest—the remnants of victims captured in mid-air and fed to the falcon chick. But as I looked at the falcons, all I could think was: *You wimps! You wouldn't be here without us! We've spent millions on you; we've banned the DDT that was upsetting your delicate systems; we've built you nest boxes; we've coddled your chicks—all to produce two dozen birds in New York. One pigeon colony achieved that in my courtyard by itself.*

21   A lot of people in the city may identify with the falcon: a ruthless, grandly isolated predator, rewarded with a penthouse view of its dominion. But the falcon doesn't hold the great secret to evolutionary success, at least not for humans.

22   Our species did not prevail over other animals by being brave and cunning solitary hunters. We used our brains to become co-operative and shameless opportunists, able to adapt to any available niche. We may pollute and squabble and crowd together in grimy crannies without views, but at least we're survivors. We may envy their speed and rapacity, but we are not falcons. We are tougher. We, fortunately, are pigeons.

Adapted from a *New York Times* article by John Tierney

[END OF PASSAGE]

[BLANK PAGE]

G

Total Mark

0860/104

SCOTTISH
CERTIFICATE OF
EDUCATION
1998

WEDNESDAY, 6 MAY
1.00 PM – 1.50 PM

ENGLISH
STANDARD GRADE
General Level
Reading
Questions

SCOTTISH
QUALIFICATIONS
AUTHORITY

Marks

QUESTIONS

Write your answers in the spaces provided.

Look at Paragraphs 1 to 5.

1. (*a*) **Write down** an expression from **Paragraph 1** that clearly indicates **the writer's attitude** to pigeons.

   _____

   2 ■ 0

   (*b*) Given his attitude, what **fact** about pigeons did the writer find difficult to understand?

   _____

   _____

   2 ■ 0

2. (*a*) "Should I smash it right away or save it for an omelette?" (Paragraph 2)
   What was Dana's reaction to these suggestions?

   _____

   _____

   2 ■ 0

   (*b*) Why is her reaction surprising?

   _____

   _____

   2 1 0

Look at Paragraph 6.

3. Why does the writer begin **Paragraph 6** with such a short sentence?

   _____

   _____

   _____

   2 ■ 0

4. What expression used later in the same paragraph means almost the same as "perennial mystery"?

   _____

   2 ■ 0

PAGE
TOTAL

5. Explain how the writer tries to make the rest of **Paragraph 6** funny.

_____

_____

_____

2 | 1 | 0

Look at Paragraphs 7 to 10.

6. What evidence is there that the writer started to take a closer interest in the pigeons?   2 | 1 | 0

(i) _____

(ii) _____

(iii) _____

7. "he brought twigs for home-improvement projects" (Paragraph 9)

(*a*) Explain exactly what Don Guano was doing.

_____

_____

2 | 1 | 0

(*b*) To what is Don Guano being compared, and what is the effect of this comparison?

_____

_____

2 | 1 | 0

Look at Paragraphs 11 to 14.

8. (*a*) Why might pigeon eggs **not** hatch after 18 days?   2 | 1 | 0

(i) _____

_____

(ii) _____

_____

(*b*) Why don't we normally see a baby pigeon?

_____

_____

2 | 1 | 0

Marks

9. What, do you think, was **the writer's attitude** to "those people on park benches who feed pigeons" and how does he reveal it?

    _____

    _____

    _____   2 | 1 | 0

10. (*a*) **Write down two** things the writer did to ensure that the eggs hatched successfully.   2 | 1 | 0

    (i) _____

    (ii) _____

    (*b*) What kind of books do you think Dr Spock wrote?

    _____

    _____   2 | 1 | 0

Look at Paragraphs 15 to 18.

11. "Wherever civilization has flourished, there the pigeon has thrived" (Paragraph 15) What fact proves this statement?

    _____

    _____   2 | 1 | 0

12. What **two** things help pigeons to navigate?   2 | 1 | 0

    (i) _____

    (ii) _____

13. Explain why "reverse commuter" is a good way of describing urban pigeons.

    _____

    _____

    _____   2 | 1 | 0

PAGE
TOTAL

Marks

14. Explain **in your own words** why poets have praised pigeons.

_____

_____   2 | 1 | 0

Look at Paragraphs 19 to 22.

15. (*a*) Why does the writer call peregrine falcons "wimps"?

_____

_____   2 | 1 | 0

(*b*) What **two** things about the way **Paragraph 20** is written show the strength of his feelings?   2 | 1 | 0

(i) _____

(ii) _____

16. (*a*) **In your own words**, explain why a lot of people might "identify with the falcon".

_____

_____

_____   2 | 1 | 0

(*b*) Explain, as clearly as you can, why the writer believes that most human beings are more like pigeons than falcons.

_____

_____   2 | 1 | 0

[Turn over for Questions 17 and 18 on *Page six*

PAGE
TOTAL

Marks

Think about the passage as a whole.

17. Complete the following sentences to show the changes in the writer's attitude towards pigeons.

    (i) To begin with the writer _____ .

    (ii) Later he _____ .

    (iii) Finally he _____ .

2	1	0

18. Tick (✓) **one** of the following words and explain why **you** think it is the best one to describe this passage. Give evidence from the passage to support your answer.

informative ☐   surprising ☐   thought-provoking ☐

_____

_____

_____

2	1	0

[END OF QUESTION PAPER]

PAGE TOTAL

FOR OFFICIAL USE

p2 ☐

p3 ☐

p4 ☐

p5 ☐

p6 ☐

TOTAL
MARK ☐

[BLANK PAGE]

0860/403

NATIONAL
QUALIFICATIONS
2000

TUESDAY, 16 MAY
1.00 PM – 1.50 PM

ENGLISH
STANDARD GRADE
General Level
Reading
Text

Read carefully the passage overleaf. It will help if you read it twice. When you have done so, answer the questions. Use the spaces provided in the Question/Answer booklet.

SCOTTISH
QUALIFICATIONS
AUTHORITY

The following passage has been adapted from an article in "The Herald".

Just when you thought it was

Stephen McGinty
faces danger to swim with the
sharks

1   There is a cartoon in the diver's locker room at Deep Sea World. It shows two sharks eyeing up a couple of divers in masks, fins and aqua-lungs. One shark asks the other, "Will we eat them?" The other replies, "No, that thing on their backs gives me wind."

2   As I bent, buckled and squeezed myself into the drysuit, the threat of a dose of marine indigestion seemed a poor defence against the flat-eyed terrors of the deep.

3   I had been assured at the North Queensferry complex that the sharks would have no wish to eat me. I did not look like their natural prey of fish, which are small, wet and flap about. No-one noticed that at the time I felt small, was drenched in sweat and couldn't stop shaking. I didn't feel like a flounder, but given time . . .

4   In the next chamber was the world's largest underwater safari: four and a half million litres of filtered sea water containing dozens of species and hundreds of fish including bass, cod, plaice, bream, mackerel, lesser spotted dogfish, conger eels, skates and sharks. The nine bigger sharks were sand tigers—the largest about nine feet long.

5   All the sand tigers have names like Stella, Bertha, Fred, Barnie and Dino. The largest is called The Preacher because most people see him and start to pray. Barnie sounded like a bundle of laughs in comparison.

6   "Mind, the big one is a bit frisky," said another diver to Stuart Bell, my scuba instructor.

7   "Frisky?" I nervously asked.

8   "Don't worry," Stuart said as he helped zip up my drysuit. To explain, a wet suit gets you wet; the water enters holes in the suit but doesn't exit, so your body-temperature heats the water, providing an insulating layer. A dry suit seals out the water allowing you to wear tracksuit bottoms and T-shirt underneath for warmth.

9   Once sealed inside our suits, we clambered into a tiny tank, containing only a few crabs, where I hauled on my aqualung and weight belt. Sinking to the bottom I struggled to gain my balance against the backwards pull of the weights and aqualung. Gripping Stuart's arm, I drained the air from the suit and accustomed myself to the sensation of breathing underwater.

10   When I was relaxed, Stuart opened the

Childhood fears are faced as a shark

hatch leading to the main safari tank. Rock walls dropped to the sandy floor 30 feet below.

11   Though the habitat felt natural, it would be impossible to view such a variety of sea-life in Scotland's brackish waters. Brightly coloured fish of greens, blues and greys darted, twisted and turned, and a giant skate flapped over the tunnel as tourists, wide-eyed in wonder, peered up as I looked down into an utterly silent world. The only sound was the rasp of my own breath and the click of swallowing.

12   Stuart descended first and I quickly followed squinting while the pressure built in my ears. Just as on an aeroplane, you can clear them by pinching your nose and blowing. On the bottom I lost balance but was supported by Stuart as I found my feet.

13   Childhood memories of underwater programmes on TV flooded in, mixing with books and magazines on sharks and the film cartoon of *Marine Boy*. Once I had gained some confidence, Stuart returned to the surface to collect underwater photographer Gavin Anderson. It was then I noticed the little four-year-old waving from the tunnel. I started to think: what if I was eaten by a nine-foot shark? Would it scar him for life? Then I put myself in his place. As a small child my only response to a diver being savaged to death by a giant shark just feet in front of me would be . . . COOOOOL!!!

safe to go to North Queensferry

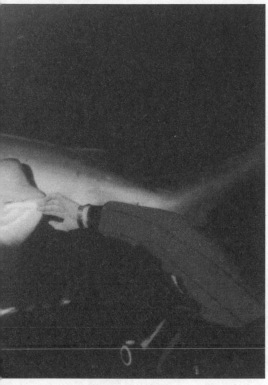

swims by, close enough to touch.

14   Deep Sea World was drawing them in with a blood-curdling exhibition about pirates. Just how much would the business boom if the sharks were to turn savage? It's all very well saying these sharks are environmentally friendly and only eat wee fish. That's boring; it's blood that the public want to see. I inched my head carefully, scanning for Stuart's return.

15   Panic and paranoia rose with my air bubbles as I caught a blurry glimpse of my foe curving around on the other side of the tunnel with a lazy flick of its tail. This sand tiger shark was nine feet long and approaching about six feet in front and above me. My lungs began to pipe the *Jaws* theme up in my throat.

16   A few images from the film looped in my head before it arrived: Robert Shaw desperately kicking at the munching mouth of the great white shark, before disappearing inside; the severed leg dropping to the bottom of the boating pond, a tumbling head, and Roy Schneider up on a sinking flag pole, taking aim and screaming, "Smile, you son of a . . . " BOOM!

17   And then it was before me in direct contrast to the celluloid nightmares of Hollywood. There was no evil eye staring me out, no prowling movement or even any interest. Instead it swam by like a bored fridge. Just then, water began to fill my mask obscuring the view. Once I had cleared it my foe-turned-

two

distant-friend was disappearing into the distance. Suddenly I felt a hand on my shoulder marking Stuart's return with photographer Gavin Anderson.

18   Gavin seemed confident and relaxed. "If we want to get a picture of you with a shark you're going to have to get quite close so I can blast it with the flash and get the shot."

19   "That won't annoy it?" I worried.

20   "What?"

21   "The shark, you won't annoy it?"

22   "It'll be fine," he said, shaking his head and administering a friendly pat.

23   Thirty feet down he fiddled with his camera while occasionally giving the OK signal—thumb and first finger in a circle while the remaining three stick up in the air. I responded, though the mouthpiece hid the manic grins I made.

24   To recap on the sunken scene, I was kneeling on the bottom with my tank to the tunnel. Stuart was stationed protectively to my left side while Gavin hung about on the right, itching to shoot. I felt like bad bait—only crowds of cod, bass and flounder flocked towards me.

25   Ten or twelve of them mobbed round my mask, occasionally touching the glass before fleeing. Then I remembered sharks eat fish and suddenly felt like jam in a swiss roll at a kids' tea party. But they wouldn't leave. Just then Gavin got excited which could mean only one thing— the return of the floating fridge.

26   Earlier, while changing, we had rehearsed how I would tilt my head backwards so that my face and the shark's would fit inside the same picture. But I couldn't do it. I didn't want to. I slightly tilted my head and noticed the soft underbelly breeze above me, close enough to touch. This was real, not an image from a movie.

27   The finest moment of a memorable dive was when we slowly rose to the surface as a giant skate flapped past on one side while a sand tiger shark browsed by below me. The chance of such an encounter in the open seas would be as slim as my chances of survival without Stuart's reassuring presence and training.

28   Breaking the surface and wrenching out the mouthpiece, I swore, and swore, and swore. Swearing is sometimes more descriptive for the indescribable as the words come charged with more impact. I had swum with sharks. Childhood fears and attractions had been relived when I touched another world. I simply wanted to return.

[*END OF PASSAGE*]

[BLANK PAGE]

G

Total Mark

0860/404

NATIONAL QUALIFICATIONS 2000

TUESDAY, 16 MAY 1.00 PM – 1.50 PM

ENGLISH STANDARD GRADE
General Level
Reading
Questions

Fill in these boxes and read what is printed below.

Full name of centre

Town

Forename(s)

Surname

Date of birth
Day Month Year

Scottish candidate number

Number of seat

NB Before leaving the examination room you must give this booklet to the invigilator. If you do not, you may lose all the marks for this paper.

SCOTTISH QUALIFICATIONS AUTHORITY

©

QUESTIONS

Write your answers in the spaces provided.

Look at Paragraphs 1 to 3.

1. **Write down** an expression the writer uses which suggests that he was having difficulty getting dressed for diving.

   _____

   2
   0

2. **Write down** an expression he uses to show how he feels about the sharks.

   _____

   2
   0

3. (*a*) What reason was the writer given for believing that the sharks wouldn't want to eat him?

   _____

   2
   0

   (*b*) Explain fully why the writer was not reassured by this reason.

   _____

   _____

   _____

   2
   1
   0

4. "I didn't feel like a flounder, but given time . . . "
   Why do you think the writer **deliberately** chose not to complete this sentence?

   _____

   _____

   2
   1
   0

Look at Paragraphs 4 and 5.

5. "In the next chamber was the world's largest underwater safari . . ."
   Show how the writer continues this idea throughout Paragraph 4.

   _____

   _____

   2
   1
   0

6. Explain fully how The Preacher got its name.

_____

_____

2
1
0

Look at Paragraphs 6 to 9.

7. Explain the difference between a wet suit and a dry suit by completing the following sentences. **Use your own words as far as possible.**

(i) A wet suit keeps you warm by _____

_____

_____

2
1
0

(ii) A dry suit keeps you warm by _____

_____

_____

2
1
0

8. Explain clearly why the writer had to struggle to keep his balance at the bottom of the small tank.

_____

_____

2
1
0

Look at Paragraphs 10 to 12.

9. Once he was in the main safari tank, the writer noticed various aspects of the fish and their world. Give **three** of them.

(i) _____

(ii) _____

(iii) _____

2
1
0

10. Apart from the loss of balance, what other problem did the writer experience, and how did he overcome it?

_____

_____

2
1
0

Look at Paragraphs 13 and 14.

11. Why do you think the writer has chosen the word "flooded" to describe how his memories returned?

_____

_____

2
1
0

12. The writer notices a little four-year-old watching him.

(*a*) Explain clearly why the writer worried about this at first.

_____

_____

2
1
0

(*b*) Why did he change his mind?

_____

_____

2
1
0

13. ". . . it's blood that the public want to see." (Paragraph 14)

What evidence does the writer give that savagery is good for business at Deep Sea World?

_____

_____

2
1
0

Look at Paragraphs 15 to 22.

14. What effects did the "blurry glimpse" (Paragraph 15) of the shark have on the writer?

_____

_____

2
1
0

15. ". . . it swam by like a bored fridge." (Paragraph 17)

Explain how effective you find this comparison.

_____

_____

2
1
0

Official SQA Past Papers
117
DO NOT
WRITE IN
THIS
MARGIN

16. **Write down** an expression from this section which shows that the writer's attitude towards the shark had started to change.

_____

17. Explain clearly what worried the writer about having his picture taken with a shark.

_____

_____

Look at Paragraphs 23 to 26.

18. What expression tells us that the writer was still worried even though he responded to the photographer's OK signal?

_____

19. **In your own words**, explain clearly why the writer felt "like jam in a swiss roll at a kids' tea party". (Paragraph 25)

_____

_____

Look at Paragraphs 27 and 28.

20. Explain fully why the writer felt that the finest moment was "when we slowly rose to the surface". (Paragraph 27)

_____

_____

21. **In your own words**, explain why the writer thinks that swearing can sometimes be more effective than using ordinary words.

_____

_____

[Turn over for Question 22 on *Page six*

DO NOT
WRITE IN
THIS
MARGIN

Think about the passage as a whole.

22. "I had swum with sharks." (Paragraph 28)

   (*a*) What evidence is there earlier in the article that he had had a childhood interest in sharks?

   _____

   _____

   2
   1
   0

   (*b*) From your reading of the article, how do you think the writer felt about sharks or his experience of swimming with them **compared with his expectations**?

   _____

   _____

   _____

   2
   1
   0

[END OF QUESTION PAPER]

G

0860/403

NATIONAL
QUALIFICATIONS
2001

MONDAY, 14 MAY
1.00 PM – 1.50 PM

ENGLISH
STANDARD GRADE
General Level
Reading
Text

Read carefully the passage overleaf. It will help if you read it twice. When you have done so,
answer the questions. Use the spaces provided in the Question/Answer booklet.

MCB 0860/403 6/71520

©

The Appeal of

1   All the junk in Scotland meets your befuddled gaze: thousands of unwanted gifts, the "wee something" for Christmas and the "I saw this and thought of you" for your birthday (how you wish they hadn't); then there are the holiday souvenirs. In short, all the stuff with which we tend to clutter our lives and our cupboards has somehow ended up in one place, awkwardly arranged on a vast number of folding tables.

2   Behind them, all kinds of people are perched on the tailgates of a variety of vehicles. Is this some bizarre store for recycled rubbish? Well, in a way it is. In other words, you have found yourself in the middle of your first car boot sale. They can be found most weekends in summer, and sometimes in winter too, in villages, towns and cities throughout the country. Sometimes they are held on an occasional basis—a charity or other organisation will hire a hall or a school playground, advertise in the local press and rent out pitches at £5 or £10 for the day. Other sales are held every Saturday or Sunday on more permanent sites.

3   Women seem to outnumber men behind the essential tables: although men often come to help to set up, they retire shyly for most of the day and return in the late afternoon to pack up the left-overs. Curiously enough, there are as many male customers as female: all human life wanders by.

4   There goes a plump medallion man who will tell you—his unhappily captive audience—a succession of unfunny and wildly politically incorrect jokes at which you will laugh, lamely, and hope he goes away.

5   There goes a succession of polite elderly gentlemen, clean and smart in their car coats; they will go off happily clutching boxes of your ancient gardening tools to which their wives will most surely object, but who are you to spoil their fun?

6   There is, just occasionally, a serious side to all this, which may affect the buyer rather than the genuine seller. Car boot sales can provide a certain amount of cover for less honest traders and it is as well to bear this in mind if you are offered a more than average bargain. Where, for instance, did those big canisters of cleaning fluid designated "Janitorial Supplies" originate? And what about those suspiciously home-made looking video cassettes of all the latest movies? Trading Standards Officers sometimes visit boot sales to keep a lookout for fakes. Police

Never underestimate what will sell. Old console games or market for all

occasionally find stolen goods lurking among the junk. Customs and Excise may be investigating those suspiciously cheap cigarettes and Environmental Health Officers may even be wondering whether that delicious home-made tablet has been concocted with due regard to public health.

7   But on the whole, say the police, they have little trouble with car boot sales. Most are legitimate and harmless: ordinary punters offloading bric-a-brac onto other ordinary punters. To a Martian hovering up there we must all look like nothing so much as a colony of ants, struggling to carry off various large and cumbersome objects, a table here, a suitcase there . . .

8   So if you fancy trying a boot sale, just for the fun of it, here are a few ground rules for participating in this most rewarding game.

9   Go as a buyer first, if you can. Have a good look around. Some pitches are better than others. Some are closer to the loos. Some are on windy corners and some may be right next to the little roundabout that plays the same four-bar tune all day long.

10   Go early, if you are selling. Many car boot sales that advertise an opening time of 10 am are being set up by seven or eight in the morning.

Car Boot Sales

videos will disappear as if by magic and there is a ready
kinds of gadgets.

11   Beware of the antique dealers. They will surround your table at this early hour like wild dogs around a carcase, fingering your Aunty Annie's floral teapot with its dripping spout and trying to decide if they are getting the bargain of the century at £1·50 including chipped lid. Remember the Antiques Roadshow. Remember that daft little pottery owl that fetched thousands.

12   Invest in a cheap wallpapering table. You can sell out of the boot of your car, but if you have as much junk to get rid of as most of us do, you will need more space than the average hatchback can supply. Take a secure container for your money—preferably a money belt so that you can keep your takings safely about your person. Don't leave handbags lying around; car boot sales are hunting grounds for purse snatchers. By the same token it's wise to take a friend. Then you have someone to mind the stall while you take time out to browse around the neighbouring stalls.

13   Don't sell old electrical goods: they can be dangerous, and you can be in trouble with the law for doing so.

14   Take lots of food and drink with you: sandwiches, chocolate bars, flasks of tea and coffee, cans of soft drinks. You will be amazed at how hungry and thirsty you will get standing around all day and there is little point in blowing your takings on hamburgers although the smell will certainly drive you wild. Wear comfortable shoes and remember to take warm clothes, even in summer. Remember to plan for rain. This is Scotland after all, and you will probably get cold and wet.

15   Don't overprice your goods, but never underestimate what will sell either. The truth is that people will buy almost anything if the price is right. Old Playstation games, or genuine second-hand videos, will disappear as if by magic. Even more surprisingly, so will large, rickety (and empty) wooden boxes, elderly baseball caps that were given free with something ten years ago, shabby plastic dinosaurs that have been in many an imaginary battle and a pile of kitchen gadgets such as the tattie peeling machine that always took ages to wash afterwards, the expensive plastic containers with ill-fitting lids and the pancake mixer that liberally sprinkled you with batter every time you tried to use it. Just lay it out and somebody will come along wanting to buy it.

16   Above all, don't expect to make any fortunes. What you will do is recycle a truly astonishing amount of junk, give an amazing amount of pleasure to all kinds of people, observe all human life wandering past your table, and come home with a modest profit. That's if you can stop yourself from filling your car boot with other people's junk before you go home.

17   After all there's a little collection of pressed glass over there that is so irresistible, and the old hand-knitted Shetland shawl that nobody seems to have spotted, and isn't that a genuine stone hot-water bottle lurking among the rubbish . . . ?

Adapted from an article in "The Scotsman" by Catherine Czerkawska.

[END OF PASSAGE]

[BLANK PAGE]

G

Total
Mark

0860/404

NATIONAL
QUALIFICATIONS
2001

MONDAY, 14 MAY
1.00 PM – 1.50 PM

ENGLISH
STANDARD GRADE
General Level
Reading
Questions

Fill in these boxes and read what is printed below.

Full name of centre

Town

Forename(s)

Surname

Date of birth
Day Month Year

Scottish candidate number

Number of seat

**NB Before leaving the examination room you must give this booklet to the invigilator.
If you do not, you may lose all the marks for this paper.**

SCOTTISH
QUALIFICATIONS
AUTHORITY

QUESTIONS

Write your answers in the spaces provided.

Look at Paragraphs 1 and 2.

1. "All the junk in Scotland meets your befuddled gaze"

    How does the writer continue the idea of "junk" in the first two paragraphs?

    _____

    _____

    (margin: 2 1 0)

2. **Write down an expression** from Paragraph 2 which shows that the writer thinks this "junk" makes a **strange collection**.

    _____

    (margin: 2 1 0)

3. Explain the **differences** between the two types of car boot sale described in Paragraph 2.

    (i) _____

         _____

    (margin: 2 1 0)

    (ii) _____

         _____

    (margin: 2 1 0)

Look at Paragraphs 3 to 5.

4. (*a*) When it comes to selling, women "seem to outnumber men".

           Write down the expression the writer uses to suggest why the men don't do the selling.

           _____

           _____

    (margin: 2 0)

    (*b*) When it comes to buying, there are "as many male customers as female".

           What is the writer's reaction to this? Answer in your own words.

           _____

    (margin: 2 0)

5. (a) The writer gives two examples of "human life" wandering by.
    In your own words, explain as fully as you can why the writer:

    (i) disapproves of the "plump medallion man" _____

    _____

    _____

2
1
0

    (ii) might sympathise with the "succession of polite elderly gentlemen".

    _____

    _____

2
1
0

    (b) Explain fully what the writer gains by using the expression "There goes . . ." to
    introduce these two examples.

    _____

    _____

2
1
0

Look at Paragraphs 6 and 7.

6. Explain **in your own words** what the writer means by the "serious side" of car
   boot sales.

   _____

   _____

2
1
0

7. (a) What do each of the following organisations look for at car boot sales?

    (i) Trading Standards _____

    (ii) Police _____

    (iii) Customs and Excise _____

2
1
0

    (b) Explain what concerns the Environmental Health Officers might have about
    any food on sale.

    _____

    _____

2
1
0

8. Write down an expression which shows that there are very few concerns about the "serious side" of car boot sales.

_____

Look at Paragraphs 8 to 14.

9. In Paragraph 8 the writer introduces the idea of giving practical advice.

How does the sentence construction at the beginning of Paragraphs 9 to 14 help to show this?

_____

10. (*a*) **Write down** the simile or comparison which describes how the antique dealers behave.

_____

(*b*) Explain what is appropriate about this comparison.

_____

11. From Paragraph 12, **explain in your own words** why:

(*a*) you should "invest in a cheap wallpapering table".

_____

_____

(*b*) you would be "wise to take a friend".

_____

_____

Official SQA Past Papers

127

DO NOT
WRITE IN
THIS
MARGIN

Look at Paragraph 15.

12. "... people will buy almost anything ..."

The writer gives several examples to prove this statement.

Choose any **two** (APART FROM GAMES AND VIDEOS).

In each case explain why the writer thinks it is surprising that anyone should buy them.

(i) _____

_____

(ii) _____

_____

2
1
0

2
1
0

Look at Paragraphs 16 and 17.

13. The writer believes several benefits can be gained from car boot sales. **In your own words** describe two of them.

(i) _____

(ii) _____

2
1
0

14. What do you think the writer is suggesting by her descriptions of the items in Paragraph 17?

_____

2
1
0

15. Why does the writer use ellipsis (...) at the end of the final sentence?

_____

2
0

Think about the passage as a whole.

16. Look at the photograph which accompanies the article.

Explain how it shows examples of the following:

(i) the writer's advice being taken _____

_____

(ii) the writer's advice being ignored _____

_____

2
1
0

[Turn over for Question 17 on *Page six*

17. Tick (✓) **one** of the following expressions which you think **best** describes the writer's purpose in this article.

Explain your choice by detailed reference to the text.

to provide information ☐   to entertain ☐

to be thought-provoking ☐

_____

_____

_____

_____

2
1
0

[END OF QUESTION PAPER]

0860/107

SCOTTISH
CERTIFICATE OF
EDUCATION
1999

FRIDAY, 30 APRIL
9.15 AM – 10.30 AM

ENGLISH
STANDARD GRADE
Foundation, General
and Credit Levels

Writing

Read This First

1   Inside this booklet, there are photographs and words.
    Use them to help you when you are thinking about what to write.
    Look at all the material and think about all the possibilities.

2   There are 23 assignments altogether for you to choose from.

3   Decide which assignment you are going to attempt.
    Choose only **one** and write its number in the margin of your answer book.

4   Pay close attention to what you are asked to write.
    Plan what you are going to write.
    Read and check your work before you hand it in.
    Any changes to your work should be made clearly.

SCOTTISH
QUALIFICATIONS
AUTHORITY

MCB 0860/107 6/67320

FIRST   **Look at the pictures opposite.**

NEXT   Think about growing up.

```
┌─────────────────────────────────────┐
│  WHAT YOU HAVE TO WRITE              │
└─────────────────────────────────────┘
```

1. "A voyage of discovery" is another way of describing childhood.

   Write about your most important childhood discoveries.

   OR

2. **Write about** the ways your experience of growing up has influenced **your** views on bringing up children.

   OR

3. Pop stars are good rôle models for young people.

   Discuss this view.

   OR

4. Think about a time you were separated from a member of your family.

   Write about your thoughts and feelings when this happened.

FIRST **Look at the picture opposite.**

NEXT Think about appearances
both usual and unusual.

> ## WHAT YOU HAVE TO WRITE

5. "I can't because everyone will look at me."

   Write about a time when you had to overcome shyness.
   Concentrate on your **thoughts** and **feelings**.

   OR

6. Extreme fashion can cause conflict
   between young people and their parents,
   for example music, clothes and body image.

   Discuss.

   OR

7. "Individual but all the same."

   Write about how **you** cope with pressure from
   friends to go along with their ideas and
   interests.

   OR

8. "You're not going out like that!"

   Write a short story *or* **a personal account**
   or **a drama script** suggested by these words.

   OR

9. **Write a short story** with the title
   "Behind the Mask".

FIRST   **Look at the pictures opposite.**

NEXT   Think about gambling and its effects.

┌─────────────────────────────────┐
│ WHAT YOU HAVE TO WRITE   │
└─────────────────────────────────┘

10. **Write an article** for a teenage magazine
    outlining the dangers gambling can have
    for young people.

    OR

11. **Write a short story** in which the central character
    gets involved in gambling to try to solve
    his or her problems.

    OR

12. "Spend, spend, spend."

    If **you** were to win a large sum of money
    how would you make use of it?

    OR

13. "A gamble that paid off?"

    Write about a time you took a chance . .

FIRST   **Look at the picture opposite.**

NEXT   Think about people and challenges.

| WHAT YOU HAVE TO WRITE |
---

14. "Those who work in the emergency services should not have to risk their lives to rescue people who take part in dangerous activities."

    Discuss this point of view.

    OR

15. "A holiday with a difference."

    Write about an activity holiday you have taken part in.

    OR

16. **Write a short story** in which leadership plays an important part.

    OR

17. In search of . . .

    Write about what **you** are looking and hoping for from life.

FIRST   **Look at the pictures opposite.**

NEXT   Think about dance and entertainment.

| WHAT YOU HAVE TO WRITE |
---

18. A hobby? A competitive event?
A form of keep fit? A good night out?
An important part of your culture?

Write about which **one** of these is true
of dance for **you**.

OR

19. Entertaining can be hard work.
Have you ever taken part in a show or a musical
as a performer, organiser or backstage worker?

Write about your experience of **one** of these.

OR

20. "Stage Fright"
Using this as a title

EITHER write a short story

OR write about a personal experience.

[**Turn over for assignments 21 to 23 on** *Page twelve*

There are no pictures for these assignments.

21. **Write about** the scene brought to mind by **one** of the following:

    ". . . fairer than the evening air,
    Clad in the beauty of a thousand stars"

    Christopher Marlowe

    OR

    "All bright and glittering in the smokeless air"

    William Wordsworth

    OR

    "Now fades the glimmering landscape on the sight,
    And all the air a solemn stillness holds"

    Thomas Gray

    OR

22. **Write a short story** with the title
    "The Broken Promise".

    OR

23. The only hope for our future
    lies in people caring more.

    Discuss.

[END OF QUESTION PAPER]

0860/407

NATIONAL
QUALIFICATIONS
2000

TUESDAY, 16 MAY
9.00 AM – 10.15 AM

ENGLISH
STANDARD GRADE
Foundation, General
and Credit Levels
Writing

Read This First

1   Inside this booklet, there are photographs and words.
    Use them to help you when you are thinking about what to write.
    Look at all the material and think about all the possibilities.

2   There are 18 assignments altogether for you to choose from.

3   Decide which assignment you are going to attempt.
    Choose only **one** and write its number in the margin of your answer book.

4   Pay close attention to what you are asked to write.
    Plan what you are going to write.
    Read and check your work before you hand it in.
    Any changes to your work should be made clearly.

SCOTTISH
QUALIFICATIONS
AUTHORITY

©

FIRST   **Look at the picture opposite.
It shows the figure of Justice.**

NEXT   Think about crime and punishment.

WHAT YOU HAVE TO WRITE

1. "It wisnae me!"

   Write about a time when you were wrongly accused.

   Explain the circumstances and your thoughts and feelings.

   OR

2. "Let the punishment fit the crime."

   "It's time for a crack down."

   "Zero Tolerance."

   Should crime be tackled in a more forceful way?
   Discuss.

   OR

3. Choose **one** of the following titles and **write in any way** about:

   Crime Doesn't Pay   The Trial   The Verdict

[Turn over

FIRST   **Look at the picture opposite.**

NEXT   Think about people and animals.

WHAT YOU HAVE TO WRITE

4. **Describe** a person you know, who is interesting but different.

   OR

5. "It's not just a pet."

   Write about an animal which makes you feel this way.

   OR

6. "A nation of animal lovers."

   Are we? **Discuss**.

[Turn over

Agree

"Certainly, I would agree that . . ."

Against

"Not everyone however believes . . .

Persuasive

"Let's look at this together."

Argument

"The arguments really need to be fully explored."

Discuss

Balanced

"You've just got to look at both sides to be fair."

Oppose

"You may disagree but . . ."

Debate

"An explanation is really needed before it would be possible to decide."

For

"All the evidence suggests that . . ."

Question

"Is it possible to consider the point that . . .

FIRST   **Look at the page opposite.**
           It gives a range of words connected with discussion.

NEXT   Think about topics on which people have strong opinions.

| WHAT YOU HAVE TO WRITE |
---

7. **Choose one** topic on which you hold strong views.

   Make clear your opinion on your chosen topic, taking some
   account of the views of others.

[Turn over

FIRST   **Look at the pictures opposite.**
               They show how photographers from the media can
               intrude into the lives of other people.

NEXT   Think about how the camera can affect people's lives.

┌─────────────────────────────────────┐
│ WHAT YOU HAVE TO WRITE   │
└─────────────────────────────────────┘

   8. "From the man in the street to the rich and famous—hasn't
      everyone the right to a private life?"

      Discuss the effect of media "interest" on people's lives.

      OR

   9. Choose **one** of the photographs opposite and
      write the story behind the picture.

      OR

   10. Write about a photograph which has special
       memories for you.

                                                        [Turn over

FIRST   **Look at the picture opposite.**
             It shows both a telephone and computer hardware.

NEXT   Think about modern communication and technology.

WHAT YOU HAVE TO WRITE

11. "Computers are fun."

    Write about your experience of using computers
    in your leisure time.

    OR

12. **Discuss one** of these topics:

    Modem madness: the dangers of surfing the net.

    or

    The mobile phone: a blessing or a curse?

    OR

13. **Write a short story** using **one** of the following titles:

    The Message   I've Got Your Number   The Hacker

[Turn over for assignments 14 to 18 on *Page twelve*

There are no pictures for these assignments.

14. Choose **one** of the following and **write in any way you wish**:

    "Things can only get better."

    D:Ream

    OR

    "Search for the hero inside yourself."

    M People

    OR

    "We are the generation that's got to be heard."

    Robbie Williams

    OR

15. "Preparation prevents poor performance."
    Everyone has to go through interviews.
    Explain clearly what you consider to be the important steps in preparation.

    OR

16. "Today's parents need to attend parenting classes
    in order to bring up their children properly."
    Do you agree? **Discuss**.

    OR

17. **Describe** the scene or person suggested to you by **one**
    of the following:
    " . . . The sun treads the path
    among cedars and enormous oaks."

    Gillian Clarke

    OR

    "she sat down
    at the scoured table
    in the swept kitchen
    beside the dresser with its cracked delft."

    Liz Lochhead

    OR

    "Pale rain over the dwindling harbour
    And over the sea wet church."

    Dylan Thomas

    OR

18. You have been asked to choose **five** items to put in a time capsule.
    Which five items would you choose and why?

[END OF QUESTION PAPER]

FGC

0860/407

NATIONAL QUALIFICATIONS 2001

MONDAY, 14 MAY 9.00 AM – 10.15 AM

ENGLISH STANDARD GRADE
Foundation, General and Credit Levels
Writing

Read This First

1 Inside this booklet, there are photographs and words.
Use them to help you when you are thinking about what to write.
Look at all the material and think about all the possibilities.

2 There are 23 assignments altogether for you to choose from.

3 Decide which assignment you are going to attempt.
Choose only **one** and write its number in the margin of your answer book.

4 Pay close attention to what you are asked to write.
Plan what you are going to write.
Read and check your work before you hand it in.
Any changes to your work should be made clearly.

SCOTTISH
QUALIFICATIONS
AUTHORITY

FIRST   **Look at the picture opposite.**
             It shows a grandmother reading a story to her grandson.

NEXT   Think about families and relationships.

WHAT YOU HAVE TO WRITE

---

1. **Write about** a person who has had the greatest influence on you and your life so far and explain why.

   OR

2. The older generation has nothing to teach the younger generation.
   Discuss.

   OR

3. Write about a single occasion when you had to make a choice between your family and your friends.

   OR

4. Write a **short story** using the title:
   Older and Wiser.

[Turn over

FIRST   **Look at the picture opposite.**
             It shows a group of people on a roller coaster.

NEXT   Think about excitement and entertainment.

> WHAT YOU HAVE TO WRITE

5. **Write about** a time in your life when you were involved in something which made you feel **both excited** and   **frightened** at
   the same time.

   OR

6. The experience of a lifetime.

   Write an article for a school magazine about an activity which
   was, for you, "the experience of a lifetime".

   OR

7. "Theme parks—value for money?"

   Do you agree? **Discuss**.

   OR

8. **Write a short story** using the title:
   Life is Full of Ups and Downs.

                                                                    [Turn over

FIRST   **Look at the picture opposite.**

NEXT   Think about looking and seeing.

WHAT YOU HAVE TO WRITE

9. "No one knows the real me."

   Explain how you see yourself as opposed to how others may see you.

   OR

10. "You can be alone even in a crowd."

   Write about a time when you felt this way.

   OR

11. "CCTV—a good security device or a restriction of personal freedom?"

   What in your opinion are the benefits and drawbacks of closed circuit television? **Discuss.**

   OR

12. **Write in any way you wish** using the picture opposite as your inspiration.

   [Turn over

FIRST   **Look at the picture opposite.**
               It shows a couple beside an area blocked off by the police.

NEXT   Think about feelings to do with danger and safety.

WHAT YOU HAVE TO WRITE

13. **Write about** your thoughts and feelings at a time when you were
    reunited safely with someone special.

    OR

14. "Our towns and cities are no longer safe places to live and work."
    Discuss.

    OR

15. Write a **newspaper report** using the headline:
    STREET SEALED OFF!

    OR

16. **Write about an occasion** when the police were helpful
    to you or a member of your family.

                                                                   [Turn over

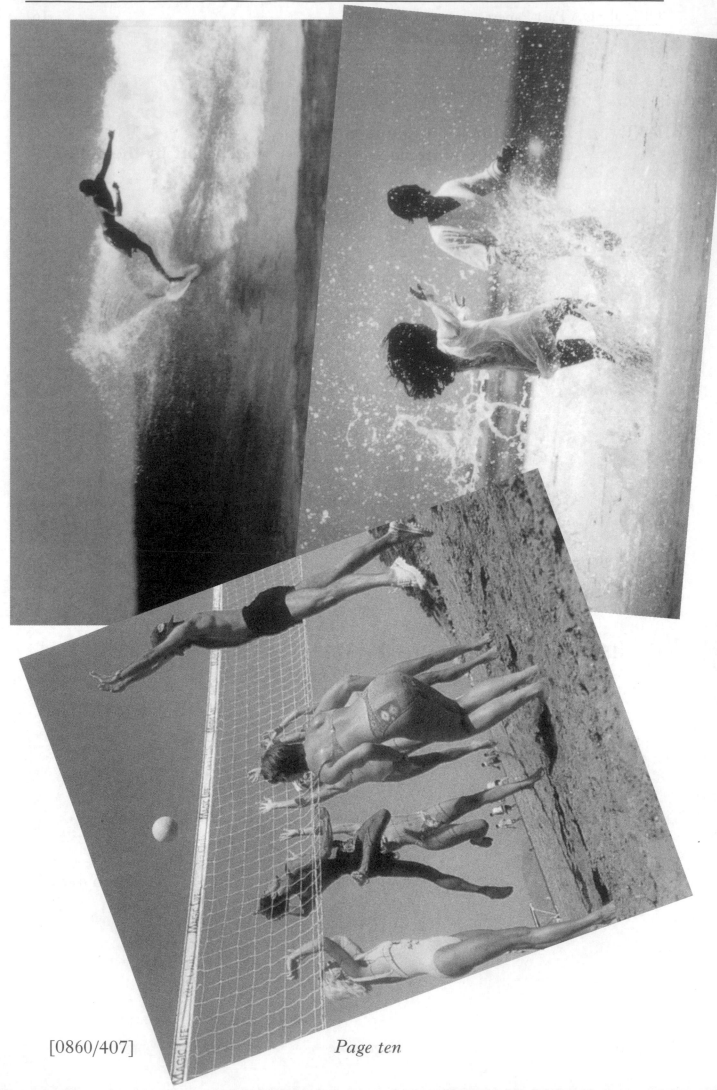

FIRST   **Look at the pictures opposite.**
           They show a variety of beach activities.

NEXT   Think about holidays.

WHAT YOU HAVE TO WRITE

17. Write about a beach holiday which you **did or did not** enjoy and which holds vivid memories for you.

    OR

18. Some of our beaches and the sea are said to be no longer safe to use.

    Write a letter to a newspaper complaining about the state of a beach you have visited and making suggestions on how it can be improved.

    OR

19. Everyone seems to want to go abroad on holiday these days.

    Discuss the reasons why you think this is so.

    OR

20. **Write in any way you wish** using **one** of the following titles:

    The Wave   All at Sea   Undercurrents

              [Turn over for assignments 21 to 23 on *Page twelve*

There are no pictures for these assignments.

21. "Children aren't children for long these days. They are in too much of a hurry to grow up."

    Is this a fair statement? **Discuss**.

    OR

22. Choose **one** of the following and **describe the scene** it brings to mind:

    When men were all asleep the snow came flying,
    In large white flakes falling on the city brown,
    Stealthily and perpetually settling and loosely lying,
            Hushing the latest traffic of the drowsy town;

    Robert Bridges

    OR

    The trees are undressing, and fling in many places—
    On the grey road, the roof, the window-sill—
    Their radiant robes and ribbons and yellow laces;
    A leaf each second so is flung at will,
    Here, there another and another, is still and still.

    Thomas Hardy

    OR

    The sky is darkening like a stain;
    Something is going to fall like rain,
            And it won't be flowers

    W.H. Auden

    OR

23. **Write in any way you wish** using the title:
    The Outcast.

[END OF QUESTION PAPER]

Pocket answer section for
SQA English Standard Grade Foundation Level
1999, 2000 and 2001

© Copyright 2001 Scottish Qualifications Authority, All Rights Reserved
Published by Leckie & Leckie Ltd, 8 Whitehill Terrace, St Andrews, Scotland, KY16 8RN
tel: 01334 475656, fax: 01334 477392, hq@leckieandleckie.co.uk, www.leckieandleckie.co.uk

English Foundation Level—Reading 1999

1. Any TWO of:

   headline/sub-headings/columns/illustration/short paragraphs

2. (a) Any TWO features of the headline. Eg Bold/bigger lettering/only key words included/(words omitted)/gives (instant) idea of the content of the article/dramatic/eye-catching/short and to the point etc.

   (b) They are a quotation/Bullimore's words/spoken

3. Any TWO from overturned (yacht)/(told him) he was not going to die/praying (that he would be saved)/capsized (yacht)/(spent four days and four nights) in an air-pocket

4. Explanation of air-pocket/how it was formed

5. Adds to drama/adds to immediacy/it's as if the reader is there/suggests story is true/sincere/adds human interest/gives a clearer picture of the man involved

   Any one

6. (a) Examples must come from paragraphs 3–5

   Eg *Heroic (survival)/(most) treacherous (parts of the world)/(stuff of) nightmares/icy waters*

(b) (i) more than 1500 miles from Australia, and

   (ii) more than 900 miles from Antarctica

7. "*solitude*"

   "*pitch darkness*", and

   "*absolute silence*"

   All three = 2 Any two = 1

8. It suggests eating a little at a time.
   It suggests he gnawed at the chocolate.
   It suggests he was saving/preserving his food stock.

   Any two

9. (a)

ACCEPTANCE	✓
REGRET	
RESENTMENT	
PANIC	

   (b) Either what he says OR how he says it.

   Eg comment on the impact of the word "well"

   OR simple statement that he had done all he wanted to do

10. (Proper) name/title/instead of inverted commas

11. (a) *they picked up a distress signal*

    (b) (i) still on upturned yacht
    (ii) floating on a life-raft
    (iii) drowned

    All three = 2 Any two = 1

12. He was in a (round the world yacht/sailing) race

English Foundation Level—Reading 1999

13.   (i)   scoured
    (ii)   expanse

14.   (i)   *"so that it would not drift away"*
    (ii)   *"and deceive the rescuers"*

15.   (i)   *"one of Bullimore's emergency beacons was detected"*
    (ii)   *"some distance from the yacht"*

16.   *"Some of the crew were dispatched in a dinghy"*

17.   Had a party
    wept for joy

18.   He does what he wants (without considering others)/(despite the accident) he will go back to sea.
    Either answer acceptable.

19.   ANY two sensible reasons Eg no photographs available/no photographer at the scene/too remote for photographer/too dangerous for photographer/drawing more vivid/only way to show Bullimore in the air-pocket etc

20.   C
    reference to paragraph 4

English Foundation Level—Reading 2000

1.   A (terrible) screech

2.   balding/scruffy/chained to perch/children teased him
    Any two

3.   (a)   snapped, flared, shrieked
        All three = 2   Any two = 1
    (b)   *"overcome with admiration"*

4.   (a)   Because he would have to be kept in a cage
    (b)   He looked imploringly at her
        He said OK/he spoke in English

5.   (after some) haggling

6.   He was grateful because the writer had removed his shackle/he was free OR rescued

7.   He couldn't fly because his flight feathers had been cut/removed (OR because he had no flight feathers)

8.   flock

9.   He soon/quickly called them by name
    Everyday he picked up new words
    Either answer acceptable

10.   Appearance—he looked healthy/his feathers grew thick or glossy/he had a confident glint in his eye
    Behaviour—he became more confident/established himself over the cats.

11.   They didn't attack Charlie (even) when he stole their food

12.   Charlie had flown although they were convinced he would never fly again

13.   Spent time in the apple tree/made a nest/would glide (from tree to tree)
    Any two

14.   He was a good listener/he could keep a secret/ they could tell him their problems
    Any two

15.   To show the speed of/shock at time passing

16.   He spoke their language and shared his apples

English Foundation Level—Reading 2000

17. Charlie behaved (or an example) in a way that showed he was enjoying himself/showing off

18. (*a*) invading (hawks)/fighter planes/bomber/signal dive-bombing/(winged) allies/ enemy

Any three = 2 Any two = 1

    (*b*) Answers should indicate how the chosen expression adds appropriate detail/drama

19. The birds OR crows flying/circling/ dive-bombing (above)

The writer and daughter shouting/ waving sticks/being in the road

20. rocketed

21. (He at last) flew high

22.

	True	False	Cannot tell
The Toppings lived in Hong Kong for 25 years.			✓
The Topping family had three dogs and four cats.	✓		
Charlie died on a Saturday afternoon.		✓	

23. Selection of appropriate adventure

Appropriate reason for being memorable

English Foundation Level—Reading 2001

1. End of winter OR start of spring

2. To show just how alone/lonely/ brave/frightened he was

3. Lying in the darkness/dust and dirt
It was as if he'd been there forever
He was pale/dried out
Any two

4. Outside doors fallen off/planks nailed across entrance/roof timbers rotten/roof sagging/floor full of cracks (and holes)
Any three = 2 Any two = 1

5. (*a*) The people who took the rubbish out of the house

    (*b*) It was too dangerous

6. Old chests of drawers/broken wash-basins/bags of cement/ancient doors/deck chairs rotted/rope and cable hung from nails/heaps of water pipes/rusty nails/cracked lino/fallen mortar
Any three = 2 Any two = 1

7. (i) the place stank of rot and dust
    (ii) couldn't bear the weight (anymore)/the whole thing was sick of itself

8. scratching
scuttling

9. (*a*)

Frightened	
Relieved	
Annoyed	✓

English Foundation Level—Reading 2001

9. (b) Michael felt he was being prevented from entering the garage
OR appropriate reference as evidence, eg He didn't want to answer his mother.

10. Because it was unsafe OR he might get hurt

11. She was annoyed because he didn't answer (the first time)

12. To show that she was shouting OR that she had given him an order/instruction

13. He didn't have time/had to hurry/didn't want to be seen/didn't want to be caught.
Any one

14. something

15. (a) million woodlice/ancient newspapers/bluebottles everywhere/ancient furniture/ dust poured through the torch beam
Any one

(b) To make it more scary/dramatic/ amazing/shocking/interesting OR mention of story-telling technique ie it's the way a child would tell it

16. (i) Michael was **scared** in case the garage **collapsed**

(ii) Michael knew he should **get out** because **they'd be calling him soon/he'd get into trouble**

17. (a)

Delighted	
Disappointed	
Surprised	
Shocked	✓

(b) My heart thudded and thundered

18. His voice squeaked

19. He was afraid of the man OR He wanted to keep his eyes on the man

20. (a) To show how unsafe it was

(b) He was afraid the garage would collapse on the man inside OR He was afraid the man inside would be disturbed/ might reveal himself/might spoil the secret

21. There had never been another creature like him in the world/he looked as if he was dead (but wasn't)/(he'd been there so long) he was covered in cobwebs OR dust OR dead bluebottles/he hadn't spoken for a long time
Any two

Published by
Leckie & Leckie Ltd, 8 Whitehill Terrace, St Andrews, Scotland, KY16 8RN
tel: 01334 475656, fax: 01334 477392, hq@leckieandleckie.co.uk, www.leckieandleckie.co.uk

English General Level—Reading 1998

1. (a) "exterminate the brutes"/
"cringed"/"cursed them"/
"winged rodents/that soil the
city"/"attacked them"
Any one

   (b) Lift or gloss of "traditional . . .
white pigeon"

2. (a) She doesn't want the egg
harmed./She is against the
suggestions./She tells him to
put them back.
Any one

   (b) Before this (in Paragraph 1)
She seemed to be against
pigeons

3. It suggests an idea occurring
spontaneously/suddenly/popping
into his head
Any one

4. "puzzled generations"

5. Reference to the Loch Ness
Monster/the Yeti
By contrasting these famous
investigations with his insignificant
one
(Idea of contrast/bathos must be
present for full marks)

6. The field journal
The fact that he gave the birds names
He notes exact dates when things
happen
He recorded their mating
Any three = 2 Any two = 1

7. (a) Making the nest better
Adding to the nest

   (b) A human being/a DIY man/an
attentive husband
For humorous effect/evoke
empathy
Any two

8. (a) "parents frightened off the
nest"
"parents aren't getting the right
diet"
eggs are not "sturdy" enough
Any two

   (b) They stay in the nest
until they are nearly full grown

9. He doesn't like them/thinks they
are strange/looks down on them
By saying he is "worried" that he is
getting to like them

10. (a) He bought/acquired/studied/
reference books
He fed them calcium/the right
diet

   (b) Books about the care of human
babies
Condensed answers, eg Child
care

11. They are found on every continent
except Antarctica

12. The sun
The earth's magnetic field

13. Normal commuters travel from the
country to the city (to make their
living)
Pigeons live in the city and travel to
the countryside (to get food)

14. **In your own words**
Their faithfulness to mates/partners

English General Level—Reading 1998

15. (a) They need human help/they have delicate systems/their chicks need coddled to survive in the city/unlike pigeons

  (b) Two aspects of style or structure such as: the use of italics/the use of exclamation marks/the use of repetition/the structure of the second last sentence etc

16. (a) **In your own words**

  Qualities that people might consider attractive, eg "ruthless" —singleminded, ferocious, showing no pity
  "rewarded with a penthouse view"—overlooks whole city
  "dominion"—has its own kingdom/territory
  "grandly isolated"— individualistic, glamorous loner
  "predator"—hunter

  Any two

  (b) One each for a gloss of two qualities humans and pigeons have in common. Eg co-operative (work together), opportunists (take chances), adaptable (flexible), etc

17. (i) To begin with the writer **hates them (or any expression suggesting this)**

  (ii) Later he **becomes interested in them/studies them (etc)**

  (iii) Finally he **admires/respects/ identifies with them**

  All three = 2 Any two = 1

18. An argument can be made for any of the descriptions.
  The marks should be awarded for the justification presented.

  Eg Informative—many facts provided about pigeons + evidence
  Surprising—unexpected nature of some of the facts + example
  Thought-provoking—the ideas on evolution/survival + evidence

English General Level—Reading 2000

1. Bent/buckled/squeezed
  Any one

2. . . . (flat eyed) terrors (of the deep)

3. (a) He did not look like their natural prey of fish

  (b) He felt he DID look like a fish because he felt small/drenched in sweat/shaking

4. So the reader can imagine what would happen (reader involvement) OR Too frightening to put into words (writer's fears)

5. Use of/reference to large numbers of fish/large amount of water
  Lists (of examples)
  Variety (of species)
  Any two

6. Its size/fearsome quality made people pray

7. **In your own words as far as possible.**

  (i) A wet suit keeps you warm by letting in water which your body heats.

  (ii) A dry suit keeps you warm by keeping out water so you can wear (warm) clothing underneath.

8. The (backwards) pull of the weights/aqualung

9. Variety/depth/colour/movement/ silence
  Any three = 2 Any two = 1

10. Pressure in the ears (overcome by) pinching the nose/blowing

11. Reference to quantity of memories/ speed of their return and association with water

English General Level—Reading 2000

12. (a) If the child sees him attacked/eaten by a shark it could have a long-term/harmful effect

(b) Young children/the writer as a child enjoy the horror

13. The blood-curdling exhibition (about pirates) is drawing in the crowds

14. He panicked/he was reminded of the film Jaws (eg he remembered music or scenes from the film)

15. Answers might refer to:
bored—showing no interest/just swimming past
fridge—bulk/coldness/colour/non-threatening or commonplace or inanimate
OR Reference to humour

16. . . . foe—turned—distant—friend . . .

17. He would have to get close (to the shark) and the flash could annoy the shark which might attack him

18. (. . . the mouthpiece hid the) manic (grins I made . . .)

19. **In your own words**
He feels he is a central part of the food which is about to be eaten (by sharks)

20. The ability/opportunity to be so close/to such (different) fish
OR Being very unlikely to meet such (different) fish out in the open sea

21. **In your own words**
It is better at describing/conveying feeling because swear words have more power.

22. (a) Reference to TV programmes/books and/or magazines/cartoons/films
Any two

(b) *Expectations*
fear/terror/ aggression/threat of violence
Reality
awesome/non-threatening/admiration/wonder/beauty/enjoyment/desire to return
Both sides should be dealt with.

English General Level—Reading 2001

1. Reference to any TWO of—use of colon (to introduce)/(a list of) examples/unwanted gifts/wee something for Christmas/birthday gift not wanted/holiday souvenirs/stuff/(which) clutters our lives/recycled rubbish

2. bizarre
store

3. *Occasional*
on a temporary site (eg rented/hired for the day)
Regular
on a (more) permanent site

4. (a) . . . retire shyly . . .
(b) She finds it surprising/odd/strange/puzzling

5. (a) (i) because he tells jokes which you're forced to listen to/which are not funny/ which are offensive
(ii) because they buy things of which their wives will disapprove

English General Level— Reading 2001

(b) She involves the reader by use of an informal, chatty tone/ sense of immediacy
OR She creates an image of a succession of people by repetition

6. **In your own words**
You have to beware of dodgy dealers OR Official organisations may be involved because of illegal activities.

7. (a) (i) fakes
(ii) stolen goods
(iii) (cheap or dodgy) cigarettes

(b) That it might not have been prepared properly/healthily

8. (. . . on the whole . . .) they have little trouble
OR Most are legitimate and harmless

9. Each is structured as a command.
OR Each begins with an imperative/ a verb/a word which tells or advises you what to do

10. (a) . . . like wild dogs around a carcase . . .

(b) It conveys effectively how they fight/compete over their share/ over the best bits

11. **In your own words**

(a) There would be too much stuff for it provides more space than the boot of a car

(b) To help you look after things while you have a break

12. Any **two**
Boxes—rickety or broken/baseball caps—free to start with/plastic dinosaurs—used or damaged/tattie-peeler—difficult to wash/plastic containers—ill-fitting lids/pancake mixer—splashes
Any two

13. **In your own words**
You can get rid of a lot of unwanted objects/contribute to other people's happiness/see lots of different people/make a little money
Any two

14. It is difficult to resist (the temptation of) buying OR the idea of one person's junk being valuable to others.

15. To show that the list could continue/be endless OR that there could be more examples

16. (i) (wall-papering) table/people are well wrapped-up/there's a friend to help out
(ii) electrical goods are on sale

17. Any choice is acceptable, but should be supported:
information—lots of facts/advice given + appropriate reference
entertainment—humorous tone + appropriate reference
thought-provoking—provides advice/reflection + appropriate reference

Pocket answer section for
SQA English Standard Grade Writing
1999, 2000 and 2001

Published by Leckie & Leckie Ltd, 8 Whitehill Terrace, St Andrews, Scotland, KY16 8RN
tel: 01334 475656, fax: 01334 477392, hq@leckieandleckie.co.uk, www.leckieandleckie.co.uk

English Writing—1999, 2000 and 2001

	Credit	General	Foundation
	The work displays some distinction in ideas, construction and language. This is shown by a detailed attention to the purposes of the writing task; by qualities such as knowledge, insight, imagination; and by development that is sustained. Vocabulary, paragraphing and sentence construction are accurate and varied.	The work shows a general awareness of the purposes of the writing task. It has a number of appropriate ideas and evidence of structure. Vocabulary is on the whole accurate, but lacks variety.	The work shows a few signs of appropriateness and commitment to the purposes of the writing task.
As the task requires. The candidate can	convey information, selecting and highlighting what is most significant;	convey information in some kind of sequence;	convey simple information;
	marshall ideas and evidence in support of an argument; these ideas have depth and some complexity; he/she is capable of objectivity, generalisation and evaluation;	order and present ideas and opinions with an attempt at reasoning;	present ideas and opinions in concrete personal terms;
	give a succinct account of a personal experience: the writing has insight and self-awareness;	give a reasonably clear account of a personal experience with some sense of involvement;	convey the gist of a personal experience;
	express personal feelings and reactions sensitively;	express personal feelings and reactions with some attempt to go beyond bald statement;	make a bald statement of personal feelings or reactions;
	display some skills in using the conventions of a chosen literary form, and in manipulating language to achieve particular effects.	use some of the more obvious conventions of a chosen literary form, and occasionally use language to achieve particular effects.	display a rudimentary awareness of the more obvious conventions of a chosen literary form, and occasionally attempt to use language to achieve particular effects.

A combination of these qualities may be called for by any one writing task.

	Credit	General	Foundation
Intelligibility and Correctness	Writing which the candidate submits as finished work communicates meaning clearly at a first reading. Sentence construction is accurate and formal errors will not be significant.	Writing which the candidate submits as finished work communicates meaning at first reading. There are some lapses in punctuation, spelling and sentence construction.	Writing which the candidate submits as finished work communicates meaning largely at first reading: however, some further reading is necessary because of obtrusive formal errors and/or structural weaknesses, including inaccurate sentence construction and poor vocabulary.
Length	When it is appropriate to do so, the candidate can sustain the quality of writing at some length. Pieces of extended writing submitted in the folio of coursework should not normally exceed 800 words in length. The overriding consideration is, however, that the length should be appropriate to the purposes of the writing task.	Length is appropriate to the purposes of the writing task.	100 words is to be taken as a rough guide to the minimum length expected for each finished piece of work, but the overriding consideration should be that the length is appropriate to the purposes of the writing task.

	Grade 1	Grade 2	Grade 3	Grade 4	Grade 5	Grade 6
Differentiating Factors	The finished communication is not only clear; it is also stylish. Attention to purpose is not only detailed; it is also sensitive. Writing shows overall distinction in ideas, construction and language. Vocabulary is apt and extensive, and paragraphing and sentence construction are skilful. In these respects performance transcends the level of accuracy and variety acceptable at grade 2.	Evidence of one or more of the qualities of distinction in ideas, construction or language is present but these qualities are less well sustained and/or combined than at grade 1. In the main writing is substantial, accurate and relevant, but it lacks the insight, economy and style which characterises achievement at grade 1.	Writing is characterised by overall adequacy of communication. It conveys its meaning clearly and sentence construction and paragraphing are on the whole accurate. There is a reasonably sustained attention to purpose, and structure shows some coherence. Where appropriate there is a measure of generalisation and objectivity in reasoning.	Writing approaches the qualities of adequacy required for grade 3 but is clearly seen to be impaired in one of the following ways: there are significant inaccuracies in sentence construction. or the work is thin in appropriate ideas. or the work is weak in structure.	Writing rises a little above basic intelligibility and rudimentary attention to purpose. Formal errors and weaknesses are obtrusive but not as numerous as at grade 6. Attention to the purposes of the writing task is weak but the quality of the writer's ideas is perceptibly stronger than at grade 6.	Writing contains many formal errors and structural weaknesses but they do not overall have the effect of baffling the reader. The conveying of simple information is marked by obscurities and extraneous detail, and the presentation of ideas, opinions and personal experience is somewhat rambling and disjointed.

English Writing—1999

Personal Experience/Descriptive Numbers 1, 4, 5, 7, 12, 13, 15, 17, 18, 19, 20, 21

Each of the above calls for personal response; while there are no genre requirements here, content must be specific and appropriate.

No 1   A specific set of experiences—candidates should concentrate largely on events and self.

A humorous response will be acceptable.

No 4   A single specific experience—candidates should concentrate on the thoughts and feelings engendered by this.

No 5   A single specific experience—the candidate should concentrate on thoughts and feelings both negative and positive.

No 7   Anecdotal exemplars are likely.   Better candidates will be aware of the social complexities/strategies of friendship.

No 12   Rubric must be interpreted in a personal way. Details of use are of paramount importance. Altruism will play a part in more sensitive responses. The rubric may be interpreted humorously.

No 13   A single specific experience—some narrative expected but personal involvement should be clear.

No 15   A single specific experience—anecdotal approach is likely but should cover more than one activity and the thoughts and feelings associated with them.

No 17   Must describe/reflect on plans, hopes and dreams for the future.

No 18   One or more of the aspects to be chosen and described as well as the role they play in the candidate's life.

No 19   Description of event, people, role played. More able candidates will concentrate on the positive and negative aspects of such an experience.

No 20   Description of personal experience—must reflect the imposed title.

No 21   The rubric restricts candidates to the choice of a single quotation and description of the scene it brings to mind.

Grade Differentiation

1 : 2   Grade 1 will be a well-crafted, stylish account and will deploy a range of skills to express perceptiveness, insight and self-awareness and to achieve or create effects, while a Grade 2 account will be soundly constructed and show **a measure of insight** and self-awareness expressed accurately. Grade 2 may not be succinct but will be **substantial**.

English Writing—1999

3 : 4   A Grade 3 response will be quite well **sustained**, with an easily-grasped **structure**, and will on the whole be correct but with a certain dull monotony.

Grade 4 responses will be structurally weak or thin in ideas but will still **attempt involvement, approaching the overall adequacy** of Grade 3.

5 : 6   Grade 5 responses may have positive features such as a runaway enthusiasm which will detract from the stated purpose but it will present the **gist** of the experience without **ramblings** and **incoherence** which, along with **numerous errors** and near-illegible handwriting are the mark of Grade 6.

Narrative Numbers 8, 9, 11, 16, 20, 22

Task specifications/rubric/purposes

The criteria demand appropriate ideas and evidence of structure which in the narrative genre involve **plot** or **content** or **atmosphere**.

No 8   The choice of story, drama script or personal account must be clear. The imposed title must be reflected strongly in the finished work.

No 9   Short story—imposed title which must be reflected in the narrative.

No 11   Short story—the narrative must include the character and the nature of the problem(s).

No 16   Short story—the narrative must feature leadership and the way in which it is demonstrated.

No 20   Short story—imposed title which must be reflected in the narrative.

No 22   Short story—imposed title which must be reflected in the narrative.

Grade Differentiation

1 : 2   Grade 1 narrative will show **overall distinction** in IDEAS, CONSTRUCTION and LANGUAGE, and will be both **stylish and skilful**, while Grade 2 narrative will fall short both in the quality and in the **combination** of skills.

3 : 4   Grade 3 responses will have an **appropriate plot**, will make use of appropriate **register** to create ATMOSPHERE or SUSPENSE and should include NARRATIVE or DESCRIPTIVE details to establish the main lines of the plot. Do not forget that lack of variety in plot and language skills is typical of Grade 3. Accuracy is the criterion to establish here.

Grade 4's **simple plot** will approach the adequacy of Grade 3 but may be poorly organised or have significant inaccuracies.

5 : 6   Grade 5's **very basic plot** will occasionally try to achieve particular effects, and it will also be poorly organised and have significant inaccuracies.

English Writing—1999

Grade 6 responses will have a combination of negative features, will be **rambling**, have **obscurities** in plot and there will be difficulty in decoding because of very poor spelling, sentencing or handwriting.

NB If candidates ignore the rubric in respect of plot or character this may place them in Grade 5 in terms of purpose ("few signs of appropriateness"), unless there are other strong compensating features ("accurate", "varied", "sensitive"). Where there are no strong compensating features this may tip the balance overall into Grade 6.

Discursive Numbers 2, 3, 6, 10, 14, 23

Task specifications/rubric/purposes

The rubrics cover controversial issues which are likely to elicit emotional responses. Objectivity is not required but a clear, straightforward presentation of a point of view is required. At all levels, candidates must deal with the specified topics.

No 2   Agree/disagree or balanced view of the issues—arguments may be based on personal/anecdotal evidence but should follow a clear line of thought.

No 3   Agree/disagree or balanced view—much of the evidence will be of an anecdotal nature but the line of argument should be obvious.

No 6   Agree/disagree or balanced view—evidence may be anecdotal/personal but the line of argument should be clear.

No 10   Imposed form of magazine article—more able candidates will observe the conventions in respect of tone and language as well as taking the stance demanded.

No 14   Agree/disagree or balanced view of the issues. Some background knowledge is necessary regardless of the stance taken by the candidate.

No 23   Agree/disagree, anecdotal evidence should be minimal. Better candidates will be aware of the difficulty/complexity of the issues.

Grade Differentiation

1 : 2   Grade 1 responses will show a **combination of depth**, **complexity** and **skilful deployment of ideas**, and will marshall evidence in support of argument.

Grade 2 responses will lack this combination of technical skill and confident tone, presenting ideas in a **less developed** or **sustained** manner.

3 : 4   Grade 3 responses will attempt an orderly flow of ideas, which may not succeed logically, whereas Grade 4 will be typically **weak in structure**, or **have thin ideas** or poorly constructed sentences.

5 : 6   Grade 5 responses will present ideas and opinions in **concrete**, **personal terms** which may be anecdotal, but are more than a bold series of unsupported, **disjointed** or **rambling** statements, the hallmark of Grade 6.

English Writing—2000

Personal Experience/Descriptive Numbers 1, 4, 5, 10, 11, 17

Task specifications/rubric/purposes

Each of the above calls for personal response; while there are no genre requirements here, content must be specific and appropriate.

No 1 A single specific experience—candidates should concentrate on the injustice of the situation described with particular attention to their own thoughts and feelings. These feelings may include emotions at the time or feelings on reflection.

No 4 A single specific person should be selected. Candidates should select both the interesting but different aspects of the person and these should be clearly described. Reflection is implicit in the rubric, as is an element of description.

No 5 A single animal should be selected by candidates. It should be noted that this offers the candidate a full range of possibilities. Clearly candidates should concentrate on the positive thoughts and feelings associated with their choice.

No 10 Candidates may choose to take a narrow or wide approach in their responses— the incident in the photograph or a larger memory triggered by the photograph. Better candidates will include reflective writing and feelings.

No 11 Description of specific experiences of using computers should be covered by candidates. This clearly allows for a range of responses. Candidates may choose to concentrate on the positive and/or negative aspects of using computers in their leisure time.

No 17 The rubric restricts candidates to the choice of a single quotation and description of the scene or person which it evokes. Better candidates will see the importance of descriptive detail.

Grade Differentiation

1 : 2 Grade 1 will be a well-crafted, stylish account and will deploy a range of skills to express perceptiveness, insight and self-awareness and to achieve or create effects, while a Grade 2 account will be soundly constructed and show **a measure of insight** and self-awareness expressed accurately. Grade 2 may not be succinct but will be **substantial**.

3 : 4 A Grade 3 response will be quite well **sustained**, with an easily-grasped **structure**, and will on the whole be correct but with a certain dull monotony.

Grade 4 will be structurally weak or thin in ideas but will still **attempt involvement, approaching the overall adequacy** of Grade 3.

5 : 6 Grade 5 responses may have positive features such as a runaway enthusiasm which will detract from the stated purpose but it will present the **gist** of the experience without **ramblings** and **incoherence** which, along with **numerous errors** and near-illegible handwriting are the mark of Grade 6.

English Writing—2000

Discursive/Informative Numbers 2, 6, 7, 8, 12, 15, 16, 18

Task specifications/rubric/purposes

The rubrics cover controversial issues which are likely to elicit emotional responses. Objectivity is not required but clear, straightforward presentation of a point of view is required. At all levels, candidates must deal with the specific topics or, as is the case in two of the tasks, convey information about a specific activity or choices and the reasoning behind such choices or course of behaviour.

No 2   Agree/disagree. Candidates may focus on the idea of dealing with crime in a general way or may choose to focus more particularly on an aspect of crime. Some background knowledge is required. Personal/anecdotal evidence may figure. Better candidates will be aware of social/political issues.

No 6   Agree/disagree or balanced view. Some background knowledge is required. Personal/anecdotal evidence may be evident but should follow a line of argument.

No 7   Agree/disagree/balanced. Candidates should choose one topic about which they have strong views. A clear line of thought/argument should be present and there should be some indication that account has been taken of the views of others.

No 8   Agree/disagree/balanced view of the issue. Candidates may choose to base their argument on anecdotal evidence but should follow a line of argument. Better candidates will be aware of the wider issues related to personal freedom.

No 12   Views/opinions will most likely be based on anecdotal evidence but should follow a line of thought, argument.

No 15   Candidates are restricted to the idea of preparation and are required to outline the steps expected. Better candidates will outline the reasoning behind such steps.

No 16   Agree/disagree or balanced view. Personal/anecdotal evidence is likely but should be used to follow a line of argument.

No 18   Candidates are restricted to outlining **5** items. This should be accompanied by a degree of reasoning and explanation of the decisions made.

Grade Differentiation

1 : 2   Grade 1 responses will show **a combination of depth**, **complexity** and **skilful deployment of ideas**, and will marshall evidence in support of argument.

Grade 2 responses will lack this combination of technical skill and confident tone, presenting ideas in a **less developed** or **sustained** manner.

3 : 4   Grade 3 responses will attempt an orderly flow of ideas, which may not succeed logically, whereas Grade 4 will be typically **weak in structure**, or **have thin ideas** or poorly constructed sentences.

5 : 6   Grade 5 responses will present ideas sqd opinions in **concrete, personal terms** which may be anecdotal, but are more than a bold series of unsupported, **disjointed** or **rambling** statements, the hallmark of Grade 6.

English Writing—2000

Narrative Numbers 9,13

Task specifications/rubric/purposes

The criteria demand appropriate ideas and evidence of structure, which in the narrative genre involve **plot** or **content** or **atmosphere**.

No 9 Short story—candidates must make clear the connection with the given picture. Some candidates may choose to focus on the content of the picture given while other candidates may choose to write the story behind the picture—either approach is acceptable.

No 13 Short story—imposed title must be reflected in the narrative.

Grade Differentiation

1 : 2 Grade 1 narrative will show **overall distinction** in IDEAS, CONSTRUCTION and LANGUAGE, and will be both **stylish and skilful**, while Grade 2 narrative will fall short both in the quality and in the **combination** of skills.

3 : 4 Grade 3 responses will have an **appropriate plot**, will make use of **appropriate register** to create ATMOSPHERE or SUSPENSE and should include NARRATIVE or DESCRIPTIVE details to establish the main lines of the plot. Do not forget that lack of variety in plot and language skills is typical of Grade 3. Accuracy is the criterion to establish here.

Grade 4's **simple plot** will approach the adequacy of Grade 3 but may be poorly organised or have significant inaccuracies.

5 : 6 Grade 5's **very basic plot** will occasionally try to achieve particular effects, and it will also be poorly organised and have significant inaccuracies.

Grade 6 responses will have a combination of negative features, will be **rambling**, or have **obscurities** in plot and there will be difficulty in decoding because of very poor spelling, sentencing or handwriting.

NB If candidates ignore the rubric in respect of plot or character this may place them in Grade 5 in terms of purpose ("few signs of appropriateness"), unless there are other strong compensating features ("accurate", "varied", "sensitive"). Where there are no strong compensating features this may tip the balance overall into Grade 6.

Free Choice Numbers 3 and 14

Task specifications/rubric/purposes

Each of the above calls for the candidate to determine the purpose of the writing and format. It is therefore important that the candidate's writing purpose is made clear in the course of the response. Writing should be assessed according to the appropriate criteria.

No 3 The rubric restricts candidates to the choice of a single title or idea suggested by one of the titles offered.

No 14 The rubric restricts candidates to the choice of a single title or idea suggested by one of the titles offered.

English Writing—2001

Narrative Numbers 4, 8

Task specifications/rubric/purposes

The criteria demand appropriate ideas and evidence of structure which in the narrative genre involve **plot** or **content** or **atmosphere**.

No 4 Short story—imposed title Older and Wiser must be reflected in the narrative.

No 8 Short story—imposed title Life is Full of Ups and Downs must be reflected in the narrative.

Grade Differentiation

1 : 2 Grade 1 narrative will show **overall distinction** in IDEAS, CONSTRUCTION and LANGUAGE, and will be both **stylish and skilful**, while Grade 2 narrative will fall short both in the quality and in the **combination** of skills.

3 : 4 Grade 3 responses will have an **appropriate plot**, will make use of appropriate **register** to create ATMOSPHERE or SUSPENSE and should include NARRATIVE or DESCRIPTIVE details to establish the main lines of the plot. Do not forget that lack of variety in plot and language skills is typical of Grade 3. Accuracy is the criterion to establish here.

Grade 4's **simple plot** will approach the adequacy of Grade 3 but may be poorly organised or have significant inaccuracies.

5 : 6 Grade 5's **very basic plot** will occasionally try to achieve particular effects, and it will also be poorly organised and have significant inaccuracies.

Grade 6 responses will have a combination of negative features, will be **rambling**, or have **obscurities** in the plot and there will be difficulty in decoding because of very poor spelling, sentencing or handwriting.

NB If candidates ignore the rubric in respect of plot or character this may place them in Grade 5 in terms of purpose ("few signs of appropriateness"), unless there are other strong compensating features ("accurate", "varied", "sensitive"). Where there are no strong compensating features this may tip the balance overall into Grade 6.

Discursive/Informative Numbers 2, 7, 11, 14, 15, 18, 19, 21

Task specifications/rubric/purposes

The rubrics cover controversial issues which are likely to elicit emotional responses. Objectivity is not required but clear, straightforward presentation of a point of view is required. At all levels, candidates must deal with the specific topics or, as is the case in one of the tasks, use the imposed format to convey information about a specific incident.

No 2 Agree/disagree or balanced view. Candidates may choose to deal with the topic from one particular point of view or take a more balanced approach to the topic. Some background knowledge is required. Personal/anecdotal evidence may figure but should be used to support the candidate's line of argument.

English Writing—2001

No 7   Agree/disagree or balanced view. Some background knowledge is required. Personal/anecdotal evidence may be evident but this should be used by the candidate to support a line of argument.

No 11   Balanced. A clear line of thought/argument should be present. While candidates may feel that one aspect outweighs the other, responses should indicate both the benefits and the drawbacks as demanded by the rubric.

No 14   Agree/disagree/balanced view of the issue. Candidates should follow a line of argument with supporting evidence. Some candidates may choose to base their argument on anecdotal evidence or contrasting evidence related to aspects of rural life but this should follow a line of thought.

No 15   Imposed newspaper format and title. Candidates should convey information relating to a particular incident suggested by the imposed title.

No 18   Imposed format of a letter. Candidates should outline those aspects worthy of complaint and offer areas for improvement. Some background knowledge is required. Personal/anecdotal evidence may figure but this should be used to support a line of argument.

No 19   Some background information is required. Personal/anecdotal evidence may feature but there should be a clear line of argument present. Candidates should indicate the reasons behind their opinions.

No 21   Agree/disagree or balanced. Candidates may choose to deal with the topic from one viewpoint or alternatively take a more balanced approach to the topic. Some personal/anecdotal evidence may be evident but this should be used to support the line of thought adopted by the candidate.

Grade Differentiation

1 : 2   Grade 1 responses will show a **combination of depth**, **complexity** and **skilful deployment of ideas**, and will marshall evidence in support of argument.

Grade 2 responses will lack this combination of technical skill and confident tone, presenting ideas in a **less developed** or **sustained** manner.

3 : 4   Grade 3 responses will attempt an orderly flow of ideas, which may not succeed logically, whereas Grade 4 will be typically **weak in structure**, or **have thin ideas** or poorly constructed sentences.

5 : 6   Grade 5 responses will present ideas and opinions in **concrete**, **personal terms** which may be anecdotal, but are more than a bold series of unsupported, **disjointed** or **rambling** statements, the hallmark of Grade 6.

English Writing—2001

Personal Experience/Descriptive Numbers 1, 3, 5, 6, 9, 10, 13, 16, 17, 22

Task specifications/rubric/purposes

Each of the above calls for personal response; while there are no genre requirements here, content must be specific and appropriate.

No 1   A single specific person should be selected. Candidates should indicate in what ways the person has influenced their life so far giving reasons why this is the case. Reflection is implicit in the rubric, as is an element of description.

No 3   A single specific occasion or specific period of time is required. Candidates should concentrate on the conflict of the situation described. Better candidates will give attention to their thoughts and feelings associated with the conflict. These feelings may include emotions at the time or feelings on reflection.

No 5   A particular experience should be selected by candidates. This experience may span a particular period of time. Responses should show both the elements of excitement and fear. Better candidates will highlight the contrasting emotions experienced.

No 6   Imposed form of an article. This title clearly allows for a wide range of responses. Description will figure greatly. Candidates should point up what made the chosen activity the experience of a lifetime. Better candidates will indicate the personal benefits and communicate personal enthusiasm.

No 9   The rubric clearly allows for a range of responses. Candidates may choose to concentrate on the more obvious interpretation of the real me covering aspects of physical appearance, dress, etc. Better candidates will be more reflective by nature entering into aspects of self-evaluation.

No 10   The rubric restricts candidates to the choice of a single occasion which may span a particular period of time when the candidate felt alone/lonely. Candidates should concentrate not simply on the narrative aspect but also on the associated thoughts and feelings.

No 13   A single specific occasion is required. Candidates should concentrate on the thoughts and feelings experienced. Some narrative and contextualisation will be required prior to candidate's focus on the description of the emotions relating to being safely reunited.

No 16   A single experience is required. Candidates should concentrate on the positive nature of the help received. Better candidates will not only focus on the narrative but also on the associated thoughts and feelings.

No 17   A single beach holiday experience is required. Candidates should focus not only on the positive **or** negative nature of the experience but also provide reasons for its vivid nature.

No 22   The rubric restricts candidates to the choice of a single quotation and a description of a scene which it evokes.

Grade Differentiation

1 : 2   Grade 1 will be a well-crafted, stylish account and will deploy a range of skills to express perceptiveness, insight and self-awareness and to achieve or create effects, while a Grade 2 account will be soundly constructed and show **a measure of insight** and self-awareness expressed accurately. Grade 2 may not be succinct but will be **substantial**.

3 : 4   A Grade 3 response will be quite well **sustained**, with easily grasped **structure**, and will on the whole be correct but with a certain dull monotony.

             Grade 4 responses will be structurally weak and thin in ideas but will still **attempt involvement, approaching the overall adequacy** of Grade 3.

5 : 6   Grade 5 responses may have positive features such as a runaway enthusiasm which will detract from the stated purpose but it will present the **gist** of the experience without **ramblings** and **incoherence** which, along with **numerous errors** and near-illegible handwriting are the mark of Grade 6.

Free Choice Numbers 12, 20, 23

Task specifications/rubric/purposes

Each of the above calls for the candidate to determine the purpose of the writing and format. It is therefore important that the candidate's writing purpose is made clear in the course of the response. Writing should be assessed according to the appropriate criteria.

No 12   The rubric restricts candidates to the use of the picture and its associated ideas as the stimulus for the writing piece.

No 20   The rubric restricts candidates to the choice of a single title or idea suggested by **one** of the titles offered.

No 23   The rubric restricts candidates to the choice of the single title or idea suggested by the title offered.